D1600433

ECO-HYSTERICS
and the
TECHNOPHOBES

By

Petr Beckmann

Electrical Engineering Department,
University of Colorado

THE GOLEM PRESS
Boulder, Colorado
1973

ISBN 0-911762-15-9
Library of Congress Catalog Card Number: 72-88583

THE GOLEM PRESS
Box 1342, Boulder, Colorado 80302

Preface

This is not a book claiming that pollution is good for you. It claims that more, not less, science and technology is needed to eliminate pollution and to clean up the environment; and that curbing science and technology is the cure that results in easing the blood pressure when the patient is beheaded. The current sentiment against technology is being fanned by a motley crowd of sensation-seeking doomsday prophets who are adept in using scientific jargon, but inept in using scientific methods. These professors of apocalyptic holocaustology present us with their fantasies and obsessions of ever increasing absurdity. They beat the alarm drums and they despair of a foolish world that does not share their technophobia.

The purpose of this book is to show that apocalyptic holocaustology is a pseudo-science, and that its professors have abandoned scientific research; they no longer search for the truth, but for ways to support the doomsday philosophy in which they have become entrapped. They ignore the counterevidence which blatantly stares them in the face.

This is not a textbook or a scientific monograph. It is a doomsday debunker. It contrasts the horror fiction by the apostles of apocalypse with the facts, and their arbitrary inferences with more objective, if less sensational, conclusions.

There is no population explosion in the United States anywhere in sight; the fertility rates have dropped below all previous record lows, and demographers conclude from the U.S. Bureau of the Census statistics that the population will stabilize within the generation of present teenagers. There is little danger from a population explosion in the developing countries, for their population, hitherto kept in check by famine and disease, will stabilize as these countries industrialize, repeating the same patterns as observed in the industrialized countries some time ago. There is no threat of a worldwide famine in the near future, because worldwide food production is keeping abreast of population. There is no reason to run out of energy; the Sun will shine for at least another 10 billion years and its energy can be efficiently harnessed. There is little reason to run out of resources, for non-renewable does not mean irreplaceable. Pollution is not an essential by-product of technology; it is an undesirable side product which can be eliminated by more and superior technology. The technical problems of eliminating pollution are small compared to the problem of the cost and how that cost can be equitably shared.

Proposals to improve the environment by curbing technology are not only unrealistic, they are also self-defeating. The environmental fanatics are giving a kiss of death to the cause of a clean environment by burying the real issues under a mountain of myths and fictions. But their actions are not fictitious, and however well intentioned they may be, they all too often lead to more pollution and more destruction of the environment. The recent power cuts in New York City during a heat wave and aggravated pollution was due to the lack of power plants (and non-polluting ones at that) whose construction has been delayed for years by the guerilla tactics of the environmental fanatics. One of the great dangers of their movement is that it may bring about a situation where the call for power and fuel may become a call for the bulldozers to rip open the strip mines and the dynamite charges to break through recklessly to the oil shale. Who will then stand in the way of the chain saws to cut down the redwoods? In case after case, the environmental fanatic is an unwitting but effective polluter, waste maker and destroyer of the environment.

The ecocult has grown on chain reactions. Rachel Carson began her book with a description of a village where the birds no longer sing. Dr. Ehrlich presents us with his visions of 125 million American deaths in the Great Die-Off in the 1970's and he assures us that the people who are going to die in the greatest cataclysm in the history of man have already been born. But these are not the limits to growth of a horror story. Computer simulations are now being run in which no less than the entire world is done in by pollution, starvation, lack of resources and whatever other genocidal methods are programmed into the simulation.

In 1967, a British scientist succeeded in stimulating an unfertilized frog's egg to develop into several live frogs. This chain-reacted into the belief that human beings will one day be capable of being duplicated with the ease of a Xerox machine and that their mental properties will be determined by throwing in genes in the manner in which a housewife adds spices to her soup. By 1971, *Time* printed a cover story envisaging a police force of Edgar J. Hoovers, and in August 1972, the *Saturday Review* printed an article by two authors who had been duped into believing that a fiction of this type will be here in 25 years or earlier. They meditate over the problem whether genes have civil rights and call for an immediate nationwide debate what action should be taken against this imminent threat to political freedom in the face of the scientists who aspire to Godhood.

I have not, however, chosen the most fantastic concoctions of the doomsday gurus as the targets of easy refutation. Instead, I have chosen the bogeys that have proved most impressive: population explosion, depletion of resources, doom by starvation, doom by pollution, lack of energy supplies, and the Club of Rome's report of threatening doom by any or all of these.

What right has an electrical engineer to stick his nose into demography, biology, chemistry and the other sciences that are abused when apocalyptic holocaustology masquerades as a science? He has the right of any man to refuse to play a game whose rules are stacked against him. The prophets of doom have shown, for example, an abysmal ignorance of thermodynamics, and they abuse its laws to concoct bugaboos of total absurdity; is a scientist forbidden to check out the story because the field is not his speciality? Are only the doomsday prophets allowed into disciplines in which they have not been trained? Their chains leading from aerosol cans to holocaust violate the laws of virtually all sciences, including probability theory; if only narrow specialists were permitted to examine their horror fiction, it would take an academy of sciences to refute their paper tigers. Apart from this overriding reason, there are also other points that have stood me in good stead. It so happened that I was interested in ecology long before the word lost all meaning. I have been around computers for some time and I am not easily scared by systems theory and Laplace transforms. It is part of my profession to examine scientific evidence critically and to infer the correct conclusions from them. It is also somewhat ironic that I should be batting as an engineer; my colleagues have always regarded me as somewhat of a freak among engineers, and with good reason, for my personal inclinations have always kept my research close to nature and far from man-made gadgets. Even so, as I began to delve deeper into some of the ecocult's allegations, I was shocked again and again by the absence of substantiation of its shibboleths. I had, for example, been brainwashed into believing that there was a population explosion in the United States; I believed it simply because "everybody" said so.

There are certain rules of politeness among scientists. They often write that an equation appears to be in error when they mean that the equation has been hopelessly fouled up. There are several reasons why I did not feel myself bound by this scientific etiquette. These things are probably a matter of personal temperament, but to my mind, it would have been hypocritical to say that the allegation of scientists aspiring to Godhood appears to be in error. It does not appear to be in error; it is vicious nonsense, and I do not hesitate to say so. Nor am I arguing with scientists, but against a group of benighted fanatics; if some of them have academic titles, so much the worse, because they ought to know better. This book is not addressed to scientists in particular, but to the same broad public that the doomsdaymongers are trying to bamboozle with long Greek words and scientific jargon. If a scientist has his little pet theory and takes it to the public with visions of American cities littered by 200,000 corpses at a time, can he ask for kid gloves and hide behind an academic title to demand scientific etiquette?

Nevertheless, I will say here what I often repeat in the text: I have no reason to believe that the doomsday prophets act against their better conscience, and I do not share their paranoia which ascribes ulterior motives and malicious intent to their opponents. I do not question their sincerity. But sincerity is not what is at issue here. Their sincerity may be of interest to the student of the True Believer, but it is totally irrelevant to the number of pollutants in the air. Nowhere has it been my intent to question the motives of the doomsday prophets, much less their personal integrity.

This book has not been financed by Big Business. The public relations departments of big business probably have no time for books such as this, for they are busily crowing that big business is a bigger eco-nut than anyone else. Nor has this book been financed by any other institution, and the reader has not paid for it previously in taxes; it was written entirely in my spare time, mostly during the 1972 summer vacation.

Just before the manuscript was ready to go to press, I received a book recently published in Britain, *The Doomsday Syndrome* (Macmillan, London, 1972) by the editor of *Nature*, Dr. John Maddox. It is an admirable book, for at long last a scientist has stood up to say "Enough!" But I admire the book not merely on the grounds in which admiration is usually rooted, namely, that the author has the same opinions as I have. I admire the book because it is written in cold blood, and the doomsday baloons are popped one by one with dispassionate precision. I have been unable to keep equally cool in discussing the doomsday drivel. But this is only one of the dissimilarities, and one which without any doubt speaks in favor of Dr. Maddox' book. I nevertheless hope that the present book will be of some use, since the line of thought is not completely identical, and the counter-examples tend to be different, though of course, in some cases they are the same, because they are so obvious. Dr. Maddox' book was evidently also written before the publication of *The Limits to Growth*, one of the major cripples begotten by the philosophy of apocalypse. I therefore hope that the present book will complement rather than duplicate Dr. Maddox' work.

I have also read a review of Dr. Maddox' book in the British press, written by one of the authors of the above computerized doomsday simulation. It starts with "How comforting it must be to live in the world of John Maddox" and the rebuke continues in these tones of wounded shock at the sin of Maddox' book.

This book commits the same abominable sin.

It laughs out loud at a funeral.

P.B.

Boulder, Colorado
August 1972

ACKNOWLEDGEMENTS

Permission to reproduce the following figures is gratefully acknowledged. The figures on pp. 37, 39, 41 and 43 are taken from *The Baby Bust* by George Grier, © 1971 by The Washington Center for Metropolitan Studies (1717 Massachusetts Avenue, N.W., Washington, DC 20036) by courtesy of the publishers. Most of the other figures are taken from documents published by the US Government Printing Office and their origins are given in the captions, as is also done with other material in the public domain. The photograph on p.197 was taken by Mr. Larry Rana of the US Department of Agriculture in the summer of 1971, and his cooperation is gratefully acknowledged.

The six figures reproduced from *The Limits to Growth* by D.H. Meadows *et al.*, Universe Books, New York, © 1972 by Dennis L. Meadows, have been reproduced without permission of the copyright owner. These figures are used here exclusively as the subject of scientific criticism, and their reproduction serves no other purpose than to render that criticism understandable to the reader, which constitutes fair use of copyrighted material under the law.

Contents

1

An Unfortunate Creation of Nature: Man

Encroachment of human activity on natural flood plains presents an environmental impact. First, encroachment can alter the environment and ecology of the flood plain; and secondly, such encroachment usually generates pressure for flood-control measures which further alter the stream environment.
Final report of the Colorado Environmental Commission, March 1972.

No reasonable person wants foul water or polluted air; but not everybody who wants clear water and clean air is reasonable.

All those who wish to do something about pollution and deterioration of the environment can be divided into two sharply distinct groups: those who realize that to clean up the environment, more, not less, technology is needed; and those who oppose further development of available technology. On an ever increasing scale, this second group opposes science and technology *per se*. It is this second group with which this book is primarily concerned, and the following chapters will seek to show that their assumptions are false, their arguments fallacious, and their methods self-defeating.

The arguments of the technophobes and doomsday prophets are a collection of deceptively simple halftruths. Natural resources are limited; population is exponentially increasing; science and technology exploit these resources at an ever increasing rate to satisfy an ever increasing population, producing ever increasing pollution and destruction of the natural environment; therefore science, technology and economic growth must be stopped, or catastrophe and holocaust, now rapidly approaching, cannot be fended off.

If this argument were totally absurd, it would hardly have been accepted by a mass movement of huge proportions; there must obviously be a kernel of truth in it. But the same could be said of the teachings of Karl Marx or the founder of nudism. Less than total absurdity is not enough for credibility.

Natural resources, as we shall see, are not necessarily limited. The primary resource, energy, is virtually unlimited. The sun's energy will be radiated for at least another 10 billion years, and if we will only spend more effort on research instead of reveling in the doomsday doldrums, we can, within the next decade, begin to capture some of that energy now escaping into space; and we can harness it without creating an ounce of pollution. The population of the United States is not anywhere near danger of exploding. The fertility rate has been steadily declining for the last 13 years. It is now very close to the value corresponding to zero population growth, and some experts predict from the figures released by the Census Bureau in May 1972 that the US population may level off by the year 2010. The reason why the population is still growing under these circumstances is that population does not grow by birth rate alone; the other reason is the increasing life expectancy of the population — they stubbornly refuse to die off in time. If the would-be population controllers were consistent, they would not preach birth control and abortion; they would preach abolition of hospitals and medical care.

But population controllers and environmental fanatics are not consistent, and they cannot be confused by the facts. To them, *any* interference with the natural ecosystem, "with the delicate checks and balances of nature," is a crime. The ecosystem, to their basic attitude, does not include Man; Man is merely an unfortunate creation of nature upsetting that ecosystem.

Yet to most others, some profound changes of the ecosystem are among Man's proudest achievements. Two thousand years ago, most of Europe was covered with virgin forest; it is now a thriving civilization. Was that a crime?

Five hundred years ago, the ecosystem was balanced by rats and lice infested with the germ of the bubonic plague. Men learned to upset the ecosystem and to stamp out the bubonic plague. Was that a crime?

Little more than a century ago, surgery was performed on patients after making them drunk and hitting them over the head with a club. Then men learned to overpower nature with anasthaetics. Was that a crime?

The Dutch reclaimed vast areas from the sea; the Israelis made the desert bloom; the Americans spanned a wild continent by roads and railways. Was that a crime?

But this is not a book of rhetorical questions. We shall in due course examine the irrational extremism of some who claim, and doubtlessly believe, that they want to improve the quality of life. We shall primarily be concerned with the hard facts without questioning the motives of the people who ignore or dispute them. The reader impatient for these facts should turn to the next chapter; but here I would like to discuss another point first: What are the deeper roots of the emotional environmentalism that is apparent in the affluent sections of the population in the most affluent countries?

We are offered some simple answers to that question. "Pollution of the environment, overcrowding, wanton destruction of nature, which has never been as bad as now." But some (not all) of these undesirable and unnecessary byproducts of technological progress have been deteriorating all the time; at any past time, therefore, things had never been as bad as then, yet no mass movement developed. "Because only now things have really become unbearable," we are told. This is not acceptable for at least two reasons. In many instances, things were very much worse than they are now. One need not go back to 18th century London or Vienna, whose streets were open sewers; it is sufficient to compare industrial safety and cleanliness, food inspection, drug control, urban planning, road safety and a hundred other indicators of 30 years ago with that of 10 years ago. But more important, if something becomes unbearable, it is usually the one who cannot bear it who makes himself heard. The calls to end racial discrimination come, and rightfully so, from Negroes and Indians in the USA, and from Jews in the USSR. The calls to end sexual discrimination come, and rightfully so, from women. But where do the calls to stop population growth come from? Not from India or South America, where population growth is indeed a problem; but from the USA, where no population explosion threatens. And who, within the USA, is hardest hit by pollution and overcrowding? The Sierra Club member caught in a traffic jam while driving to his golf course, or the ghetto inhabitant living in rat-infested quarters next to the belching smoke stacks of his city? Yet the latter, from all available evidence, usually considers environmentalism as just "another racket of Whitey's world." The typical environmentalist lives in the suburban fashionable split-level home; and with the air conditioner and the kitchen range running at full power, he or she is firing off indignant letters to the local power company to stop the pollution.

Obviously, then, the roots of environmental extremism go deeper than merely environmental extremes. In particular, those who oppose science and technology as such, cannot have been brought to their state of mind by rational concern about the environment; for even the flimsiest investigation will quickly reveal that more technology is urgently needed to lower pollution levels. As a matter of fact, more technology is urgently needed even to *measure* them reliably.

Throughout history, there have been groups regarding science and technology as evil and blaming scientists for whatever abuses their discoveries and inventions may have engendered. Only once in the history of Western civilization did this attitude become the policy of the ruling powers for a prolonged period: In the Middle Ages, when the Church regarded all scientific research as work of the devil and mercilessly persecuted it by torture chamber and the stake. During the better part of a millenium, depletion of resources was negligible; the ecosystem, including rats, lice, germs and wolves, went virtually untouched; population growth was kept in check by periodic famines and outbursts of the plague, and by a life expectancy of about 25 years. But the "quality of life," by whatever means one wishes to define that nebulous term, was surely lower than during any other period in history. The nightmare of the Dark Ages was finally ended by scientific inventions and ventures: the discovery of the New World and the other major maritime expeditions, the printing press, and the invention of gun powder. (No opinion is offered here whether the invention of gun powder was a "good" or a "bad" thing. It happened; and it was used or abused for good and bad purposes.)

But the Middle Ages were not the only period in which there was opposition to scientific research. There were numerous cases of opposition to science in both ancient and modern history, and in other civilizations which had no precise equivalent to the Dark Ages in the West. In most of these, the opposition was ideological or religious, but in the early 19th century, violent opposition to technology had economic motives. During the early stages of the Industrial Revolution, the predicament of the industrial workers was shocking: an 18-hour work day; child labor; virtually no safety measures; overcrowding; squalor; poverty; disease. In a sense, the industrial worker of the early Industrial Revolution was worse off than the slave in the ancient world, for at least it was in the self-interest of the slave owner to feed his slaves. England was the first country to go through the industrial revolution, and the predicament of her workers was particularly aggravated during the latter years of the Napoleonic wars and the slump following them.

During those years the workers, who associated their plight with the newly introduced machinery, rioted and smashed machinery in angry and understandable frustration. These riots (1812—1818) are known to history as the Luddite riots, taking their name from one Ned Ludd, a Leicestershire idiot who smashed some stocking frames about 1782.

For lack of a better name, I have called the contemporary zealots opposed to science and technology Neo-Luddites. What they have in common with the original Luddites is their hatred of technology, their partial success in destroying it, and their inability to differentiate between correlation on one hand, and cause and effect on the other. But there the similarity ends. The Luddites were illiterate, starving, and driven by desperation. The Neo-Luddites, as often as not, have college degrees, they reap the benefits of the technology which they allegedly despise, and they are driven neither by desperation nor reason, but by a fashionable cause which they have ardently embraced.

The opposition of the Neo-Luddites to science and technology is not economic, but ideological. It has grown not only on the myths that "technology means pollution" and "technology got us into this mess." It has grown simultaneously with the proliferation of exotic cults regarding technology as evil, and with the rise of mysticism and the occult. One of the big sins of the Neo-Luddites is sweeping generalization, and I do not propose to counter them by the same sin committed in a different garb. I do not claim that all environmental fanatics and Neo-Luddites are mystics and believers in the occult. Yet fear of generalization should not blind one to the fact that the same age that has produced and aversion to science and technology has also seen a boom of astrology, witchcraft, satanism, spiritualism, exotic religions of every description, gurus, charlatans, magicians, hypnotists, sorcery, black masses, alpha waves and every other type of "vibes," parapsychology, psychedelic trash, religions based on LSD, the weird, the bizarre, and the occult. In what other age would a sick book like *The Exorcist* make the bestseller list and remain there for 12 months? Professor Charles Reich, champion of non-homogenized peanut butter and Consciousness III, has made up a long list of what Yale University lost before the "new knowledge" came along. The list of this grievous loss is too long to be repeated here, and I note only the following items: adventure, clothes, worship, magic and mystery, awe, wonder, reverence, fear, dread, awareness of death, spontaneity, romance, ceremony and ritual, mind-expanding drugs, multimedia experiences, inner life, wholeness, expanded consciousness, conflict, disorder, suffering, pain, transcendence, myth making and telling, bare feet...

Of course, Reich's book of wonderland is now passé, buried under mountains of fresher assaults on reason. They come and are soon forgotten, but some of their odor remains. "We have too much technology" is one of the clichés to be found in all of them. And it has made inroads. Enrolment in engineering and the hard sciences is down — the only place where experts for combating pollution can be trained. Reputable universities give courses in astrology. University departments organize environmental and ecological seminars which present only the doomsday point of view; typically, they include little more than the books by the Ehrlichs, Commoner and Hardin, second-hand versions of *World Dynamics* and the *Limits to Growth*, and biased anthologies of short extracts selected from the works of various authors from Malthus to, once again, Ehrlich. No opportunity to wave scary bogeys is missed: The cover on Commoner's book *Science and Survival* depicts a woman pushing a baby carriage; both woman and baby are wearing gas masks. The jacket of *World Dynamics* shows the curves of population and quality of life crossing as a few human figures increase to many, receding into a growing darkness, presumably symbolizing pollution and death. The inside pages of these books are equally gloomy, constantly harping on the motive of doom and holocaust.

"A ship has hit the rocks and is sinking," writes Paul Ehrlich in *The Population Bomb*. "The passengers scream for help. Some jump overboard and are devoured by sharks..." And so on. The parable ends with "That about sums up the situation on the population control front in the United States..."

"People are in the position of a wild animal running from its pursuers," writes J.W. Forrester in *World Dynamics*. "The wild animal flees until he is cornered, until he has no more space. Then he turns to fight, but he no longer has the room to maneuver. He is less able to forestall disaster than if he had fought in the open while there was still room to yield and dodge. The world is running away from its long term threats..." These gloomy seminars do not discuss the point that we are not wild animals, and therefore we can cut the fence to prevent being cornered; they revel in the doomsday doldrums and in the self-pity of the unheeded Messiah whose warnings are not obeyed by a frivolous and foolish world.

There are some blatant examples of such seminars, but I do not think that all the blame should be laid on their organizers. They are no more brainwashed than the students who clamor for this type of seminar, and both sincerely believe that they are doing the world a good turn; both exude the messianic enthusiasm of the True Believer.

WORLD DYNAMICS

Jay W. Forrester

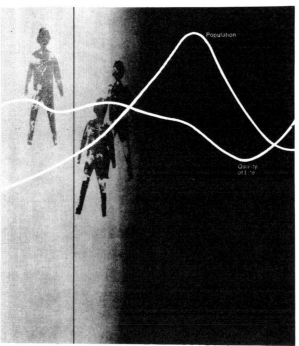

Eco-Catastrophe!

Paul R. Ehrlich

from Ramparts

In the following scenario, Dr. Paul Ehrlich predicts what our world will be like in ten years if the present course of environmental destruction is allowed to continue. Dr. Ehrlich is a prominent ecologist, a professor of biology at Stanford University, and author of The Population Bomb *(Ballantine).*

The end of the ocean came late in the summer of 1979, and it came even more rapidly than the biologists had expected. There had been signs for more than a decade, commencing with the discovery in 1968 that DDT slows down photosynthesis in marine plant life. It was an-

In all this emotional business it is often forgotten that there was a science called ecology before the word lost its meaning. (The City of Boulder, Colorado, now has an employee with the proud title *Ecology Officer*. He appears to be in charge of trash collection.) Though it may have to look for a new name, because its own was stolen, the science as such continues. With all those people wanting to be "involved," with everybody talking environment and ecology, is ecology and environmental science booming? Not at all. For it does not offer the one thing all the instant ecologists are looking for: the doomsday doldrums. Professor Keith Frye of the Department of Geophysical Sciences at Old Dominion University reports on an offered course, Introduction to Environmental Science, which he was to teach. Thousands of students took part in the hullabaloo of Earth Day, but only 5 out of the 10,000 students on campus enrolled in the course, which had to be canceled for lack of interest. Writing in the *National Observer* of October 2, 1971, Professor Frye reports "I asked one of my classes how many members would be interested in obtaining a degree in environmental science; two students raised their hands. When I began to list the courses that would be required, those two hands quickly dropped." He also concludes that "the average environmentalist knows as much about environmental science as the average Jesus freak knows about theology. And they prefer to keep their ignorance." Elsewhere he writes "The environmental sciences have not yet developed adequate sophistication to lay the foundations for comprehensive environmental engineering. Work, not student hurrah, is needed to acquire full comprehension of how the world system operates and how we might best fit into it." No wonder the instant ecologists will not enrol in the courses of such a heretic: The man's statements positively smack of honest scientific work.

But again, the students cannot be blamed. They have had less opportunity and less training in distinguishing science from emotionalism than many of their teachers who are now screaming imminent doom and pestilence.

The irrationality of the Neo-Luddites is patently evident, yet the constant repetition of the stop-the-growth-of-technology arguments has numbed some of us to their absurdity. If someone were to blame the farmer for widespread obesity,* he would make us laugh. Yet it

---

* This very apt analogy is due to J.G. Truxal, *Introductory Systems Engineering*, McGraw-Hill, New York, 1972.

has become quite acceptable to blame the scientists and engineers for all the evils caused by the abuses of science, and for some evils that have nothing to do with science as well. If someone were to blame the Crucifixion on the existence of hammers and nails, no one would take him seriously. But if the technology is more modern and the abuse contemporary, everybody sighs "Ah yes, technology has gone too far..."

There is little doubt left in world opinion, and in the opinion of an increasing section of the American public, that the most blatant abuse of contemporary technology is the Viet Nam war. Thousands of peasants have been burned alive and vast areas of South East Asia have been laid waste. It is evident that the Vietnamese no longer care whether they are ruled by a corrupt government in Saigon or a totalitarian government in Hanoi; their one concern is mere survival. Among its many other evils, that war has allowed the one remaining empire of the contemporary world, the Soviet Empire, to test its weapons without loss of life, and to pose as the champion of the underdog.

The horrors of the Viet Nam war have turned many people into blind pacifists; others equate war with technology, and an unholy alliance of blind pacifists and technophobes is being born. In several instances, this alliance has threatened the security of the democratic world, and the outlook is for a very real danger to that security. The blind pacifist is a cop-out: He would not have fought with Washington and Jefferson; he would not have fought with the peoples of Europe against the Nazis; and he will not fight against future conquest and oppression by the Soviet Empire. Like the econut, who unwittingly, but effectively, encourages destruction of the environment, the pacifist unwittlingly, but effectively, encourages conquest by war.

THERE is one thing every movement based on faith rather than reason needs to be effective: a devil. A devil to keep the followers frightened, to raise righteous indignation, and to act as a lightning conductor and scapegoat. Machiavelli may have been the first to enunciate this principle explicitly, but it had been known long before his time. The priests and medicine men of the Egyptians, Romans, Greeks, and all Indian tribes used it. No doubt it was used by whoever was in charge of the rites as Stonehenge.

The Nazis used the Jews for devils; they were not the first nor the last to do so. The High Priests of Marxism-Leninism have created a motely assortment of devils: hirelings of international reaction, imperialist lackeys, double-faced henchmen, and so forth. A particularly cute species of Soviet-invented devil is the "objectivist" — a man criminally void of prejudices. Another species is formed by the capitalist devils of Wall Street who, when not engaged in counting the profits extorted from the toiling masses, rack their brains on how to lower the milk yield in the Voronezhskaya region.

The environmental fanatics have a devil, too: Big Business. There are profits to be made in pollution, goes the story, and *profit*, as every one knows, is a dirty word. The world owes me a living, is the modern philosophy, and who has more money than big business to provide it? The mighty automobile industry never pressed the city of Detroit to construct a modern sewage treatment plant, charges Ralph Nader in an article called *The Profits in Pollution*, and goes on to charge that a paper read by Chrysler's vehicle emissions specialist at a meeting of the Society of Automotive Engineers borders on "technical pornography" because it did not deal with such things as rubber tire pollutants. In an age where equal opportunity for all is no longer understood as "I want to make it, too" but as "don't let anybody else make it, either," these tactics are very effective, and business is an ideal scapegoat.

Nevertheless, the idea of big business cast in the role of the big devil is amusing. There has hardly been such an obliging devil before. When the Jews were cast in the role of devil, they did not shout Nazi slogans, and the devils of Wall Street have not yet been heard clamoring for the eternal unity of workers and peasants. But the ecocult has found itself a very obsequious devil. "Let's Be Eco-Logical!" screamed the giant streamers of supermarket chains while the phosphate craze was on and their shelves were full of *Ecolo-G* and other powders that contained no phosphates or anything else of much use to wash the laundry with. Ecology, environment, societal needs and relevance, crow the public relations departments of big business. To whom are run-away urbanization, environmental pollution and ecological imbalance the overriding problems? To Henry Ford II. Failure to cope with these, he warns, could lead to deepening crises. The crisis is deepening whether we cope with it or not, say the computer curves of apocalyptic simulations. Financed by the Volkswagen Foundation and some of Europe's richest businessmen.

God's kingdom will cleanse the earth of all harmful pollution, transforming it into a global Paradise

ECOLOGY LITTER BIN FOR YOUR CAR

Extra-spacious • Tip- and leak-proof • Fits any car • Unbreakable • In green or black, both with white ecology flag imprint.

$2.95 Pre-paid

Ecology makes strange bedfellows. The three examples from the crowded ecological bandwagon are taken from a brochure of a fundamentalist sect, a mail order business, and what appears to be a Maoist brochure, *The Earth Belongs to the People — Ecology and Power*, Peoples Press, San Francisco (1970). "Bad ecology," says this brochure, "cannot be separated from inflation, racism, the repression of women, starvation or wars of aggression."

However, though the Club of Rome and the Volkswagen Foundation shelled out money for a very inferior product, the fact is that big business is often lavishly funding research and development of methods to curb and eliminate pollution, and that is an activity from which everybody benefits. Unfortunately, this seems to be unknown to the public relations departments of business, who have discredited its image by trying to capitalize on the eco-fad. Ecology ashtrays, ecology litter bins and ecological trash bags are now being marketed, and TV commercials peddle ecological gasolene. The power industry, for example, is investing heavily in research and development of pollutionless power generation. But its public relations departments have not found this interesting. They have been trying to get on the ecological bandwagon seeking to persuade the consumer that your local power company is your local econut, but they have done little to press home the dimensions of the looming energy crisis, and practically nothing to enlighten the public on the fallacies of "thermal" pollution or on the possibilities of generating power with little or no pollution.

This is not to suggest that big business does not wage a surreptitious struggle against environmental extremism in unclean backroom deals, or that it does nothing when its toes are being trodden on. But big business is not the only one to squeal and abandon its professed principles when its own toes are being trodden on. High minded principles quite often go out the window by pressure on down-to-earth toes. In the sixties, many affluent people in need to embrace a cause found a much simpler and more worthy cause to be embraced: the liberation of black America. They traveled to Selma to demonstrate against the brutality of the Alabama police; they volunteered to register Negroes for voting in the South; they exposed the hypocrisy of Southern whites who objected to busing when their chidren were being bused past several black schools to their own white school. This, I believe, was a worthy cause. But when it came to their own children being bused? Many of these same people found a new cause to be embraced: ecology. They are now, with equal fervor, preaching doom and pestilence if more power stations are constructed; thermal or nuclear, there is always something wrong with them. But what when the first brown-outs strike, and later, perhaps, blackouts? Will they say yes, this is what we wanted, or will they find a new ego trip to go on?

The linking of the environmental movement with issues of civil rights and minorities may be considered shockingly far fetched. Yet there is more to this link than psychological similarity.

In "ecological backlash," big business has improbable allies: leftists, radicals, and most embarrassing of all, the poor, who are hardest hit by pollution and overcrowding. Not big business, but America's poor and the underdeveloped countries of the world are the ones whose voices are heard most loudly in "ecological backlash." The poor are more concerned with the loss of jobs resulting from the failure to build the SST than with sonic booms; and the underdeveloped countries are more interested in rapid industrial growth than in doomsday theories or even scrubbers. Unlike big business, both the underdeveloped countries and the poor are making themselves heard.

In 1971, the representatives of poorer nations met in Founex, Switzerland, to air their fears that the industrialized countries would impose their new environmental consciousness on them and stunt their growth. "There may be serious distortions in the allocation of aid funds to various projects," says their report, "in view of the growing environmental concern in the industrialized countries and its unthinking extension to the context of the developing countries."

America's poor are making themselves heard on this point, too. Richard Neuhaus, in *In Defense of the People*, writes "The delight in achieving an organically pure eco-diet is frivolous in a world where twelve thousand brothers and sisters die from starvation each day." A representative of the National Committee Against Discrimination in Housing says "local communities who don't want low-income people in their areas raise the issue of growth and find allies among good-hearted environmentalists." The decision by the Livermore, California, electorate to stop its growth by banning new housing was attacked by one writer as a "de facto racist action." In 1970, city officials in Lawton, Oklahoma, attempted to block a housing project by a court injunction on the grounds that the site should be preserved as a park. The court ruled against the city after it found that the park proposal was made only after the housing project got started. The lawyer defending the project, which was sponsored by the local Catholic diocese, said "The environmental issue is raised in one way or another in virtually all cases involving challenges to exclusionary zoning." In *The Closing Circle*, Barry Commoner, an early environmentalist who has not kept up with the hysterics of the movement, condemns population control as repression, and he points out that the ecology movement's exhortations to consume less are not "likely to make much sense to blacks or anyone concerned with social justice."

The public relations departments of big business have not always reprinted the slogans of the ecocult. The Mobil Oil Company has reprinted, as environmental advertisements, some articles by Peter Passell, whom the Wall Street Journal describes as "a bearded Columbia professor who started pumping for growth when he decided revolution wasn't imminent."

But the Mobil Oil Company is not the only representative of America's poor. Where pollution and overcrowding are concerned, the poor can also rely on the Sierra Club. According to Professor Richard Behan of the University of Montana, 80% of its members do professional or managerial work, and 30% earn more than $18,000 a year. Now contrary to contemporary fashion, I do not consider it a crime to make more than $18,000 a year. But it has always struck me as a trifle funny when male doctors lecture women on painless childbirth, or when the Soviet press lectures Americans on free elections. It strikes me as equally funny when the well-to-do lecture the rest of the population on the evils of overcrowding, the benefits of organic diets, the importance of preserving alligators, and the need to stunt all industrial growth. I suspect that the poor are less amused, particularly by the latter proposition.

In short, the poor are the hardest hit by pollution and overcrowding; the affluent have organized to stamp out these evils; and the primary victims are shouting back "Don't be so good to us!"

WHAT are the roots of all this irrationality? Why do people who are indifferent to the daily massacres of the Viet Nam war, to the torture of political prisoners in the USSR or South Africa, to poverty and squalor in their own communities, suddenly become "involved" and "turned on" when it is a matter of preventing the construction of a power station that they will need? Why have they turned against technology which has enriched their material and spiritual lives? Why are they panicking about doomsday instead of clamoring for more scientific research to prevent it?

Unlike the econuts, I do not have all the answers. I have pointed out some of the symptoms above, but none of the deeper causes. I do not know the deeper causes. Whilst the following chapters will be concerned with hard facts and peoples' actions, they will not be concerned with their underlying motivations, which are in all probability unknown to these people themselves. This is a field for psychologists into which, beyond the following few remarks, I will not venture.

It is doubtful that the explanation is simple, or that there is a unique answer. No doubt the urge of conformity plays a certain role in the psychology of the instant ecologist, as it plays one in all fads and uncritically accepted opinions. Psychologists are agreed that the urge for conformity is much stronger than most people realize; some put its strength next to the urge for self-preservation and the sex urge. But the urge to conform does not explain the origins of what is being conformed to.

The psychology of the doomsday prophet is perhaps not the biggest puzzle that confronts the student of the ecocult. Especially among the most radical apostles of apocalypse, one often finds the young and inexperienced ex-scientist who was a mediocrity in his original field. His theories are founded in such flimsy and one-sided evidence, and sometimes in no evidence at all, that one can soon discard the theory that his obsessions are rooted in dispassionate and patient scientific research. More likely, he is taking the short cut to glory. Death is frightening and interesting, and he is the man in the know: He becomes Medicine Man and Messiah in one. He does not use voodoo dolls, but digital computers; but like the voodoo sorcerer, the doomsday prophet becomes the first victim of his own superstitions and the first to believe in them. He is not a conscious swindler, but a True Believer. He issues his warnings and prescribes his remedies in all sincerity.

But this interpretation, whether right or wrong, does not explain the mass following which the doomsday prophets enjoy. Among many possible explanations, Toffler's theory seems highly plausible, although it is hardly the only one and probably incomplete. In his study *Future Shock,** Alvin Toffler points out that modern man, far from becoming a dehumanized number in an automated society, is faced with such an overwhelming choice of goods, services, entertainment, information, ideologies, and above all, personal decisions, that he can often no longer take it without psychological damage. Toffler calls this *overchoice.* He further points out that the rate of development of society, technological or other, is constantly being accelerated, and is now so fast that the future, as it were, arrives earlier than people are able to adapt to it; he calls the resulting psychological damage *future shock.*

Toffler's study also describes the victims of overchoice and future shock. Although it does not deal with the ecocult in particular, the

---

* Random House, New York, 1970; paperback edition: Bantam Books.

symptoms mentioned by Toffler are unmistakable. Writing about the diversity of subcults forming in modern society, Toffler writes (condensed here) "Subcults reach out to capture us and appeal to [us] in ways far more powerful and subtle than any yet devised by Madison Avenue. They offer not a product, but a superproduct. The 'miracle ingredient,' the exclusive component, the one thing that subcults offer that other hawkers cannot, is a respite from the strain of overchoice. For they offer not a single product or idea, but a way of organizing all products and ideas, not a single commodity, but a whole style, a set of guidelines that help the individual reduce the increasing complexity of choice to manageable proportions. Most of us are desperately eager to find such guidelines."

Does a connection click between the ecocult and the simultaneous appearance of all the other cults, from witchcraft to alpha vibes?

There is, of course, one important difference between the econut and the members of the other cults: The econut has a respectable peg on which to hang his hat. Whilst the witches, satanists, vibe fans and spiritualists meet in secret for their incantations, rites and meditations, the econut can publicly beat himself in the chest with messianic righteousness. If he takes to the streets to unseat the establishment, he is liable to get his head busted, and if he joins one of the new exotic religions, he is liable to make himself ridiculous; Jerry Rubin, for example, considers it a religious act to urinate on the Pentagon. But if he joins the ecocult, he can not only cater to his hang-ups, he can also earn the respect of his fellow citizens, for who would oppose clean air and clear water?

But back to Toffler. He categorizes victims of future shock into the following four most common types: the Denier (who refuses to acknowledge new realities), the Specialist (who keeps up with novelty only in a special field), the Reversionist, and the Super-Simplifier. The latter two categories appear particularly relevant to the ecocult. The Reversionist "demands, in one masked form or another, a return to the glories of yesteryear." According to Toffler, the law-and-order advocates of the right and at least some parts of the radical left share a secret passion for the past. However this may be for political outlooks, the passion for the past is too conspicuous to be missed in the case of both environmental fanatics and Neo-Luddites. Toffler used the words "the exaggerated contempt for science and technology" in describing the psychology of youthful left-wing reversionists, but do they not fit the environmental extremists and Neo-Luddites just as well?

As for the Super-Simplifier, the term is probably self-explanatory, and an apt description of both econuts and Neo-Luddites. Science and technology are the roots of all evil; abolish them. Phosphates cause eutrophication; prohibit them. And of course, legislate, legislate, legislate. All evils can simply be prohibited by law. Do phosphates hurt running waters? Will non-phosphates lead to increased pollution through decreased effectiveness and increased amounts per wash? Are non-phosphates a health hazard? Such questions are never asked by the super-simplifiers.

It is also interesting to note how little the Reversionists and Super-Simplifiers have changed over the better part of two centuries separating periods of increased stress. We are now crossing the threshold of a Second Industrial Revolution. The first industrial revolution was based on artificial forces generated by mechanical machines; the second will be based on the artificial intelligence that can be built into the software of digital computers. In the vast majority of cases, computers are now being used merely to store information and to perform logical and arithmetical operations by slavishly following the instructions of their programmers. But this harnesses only a small part of the true potential of digital computing. Computers can be made capable of learning (from other computers, by rote, by studying evidence, from their previous errors, etc.), of independent decision making, of writing programs to write programs, of adapting to unforeseen circumstances, and of exhibiting all essential characteristics of intelligence. The critical line where computers exhibit more intelligence than the men who programmed them (albeit in very narrow fields), has already been crossed, and the only reason why the Neo-Luddites have not yet raised an ear-shattering scream of "Destroy them!" is that they have no inkling of what is going on at John Hopkins or Caltech. Yet this is no secret, and certainly nothing to be ashamed of; the information is available to anyone who is interested.*

The transition of artificial intelligence from laboratory to general society will, naturally, result in a period of stress. The fact that within a very few years the storage facilities of computers will have surpassed those of the human brain in both density and access times will shock many people, just as it shocked many people that the Iron Horse could run faster and longer than natural horses. The Deniers did not admit that the Iron Horse could be as good or better than

---

* See, for example, J.R. Slagle, *Artificial Intelligence*, McGraw-Hill, New York, 1971.

the natural horse, and the Deniers will not admit that artificial intelligence can be as good or better than natural intelligence. Artificial intelligence, predictably, will not only be used but also abused, just as the machines of the first industrial revolution were, and are, both used and abused.

The similarities between the victims of this stress, then and now, are unmistakable. Then and now, many were unable to distinguish between use and abuse. Like the proverbial cuckold who, on finding his wife in bed with the milkman, kicked the milkman's horse in the stomach, they vent their frustration in the wrong place. They turn against technology. The Luddites smashed a few pieces of machinery; the Neo-Luddites have decimated the aerospace industry, curbed funds for basic research, and made science and technology dirty words in the eyes of a considerable part of the younger generation. The differences are not essential: The Luddites were hanged; the Neo-Luddites are receiving honorary degrees.

But even those differences vanish when it comes to the Reversionists and Super-Simplifiers. "Back to the land!" cried William Cobbett (1763—1835) as a cure-all for the first industrial revolution. "Back to the land!" cry the reversionists as a panacea for the urban crisis, in nostalgia for the rural America that has gone for good. "Too many people!" said Thomas Robert Malthus (1766—1834), the dean of the super-simplifiers. "Too many people!" say the ZPG fanatics. The Malthusians advocated, and succeeded in, breaking up families condemned to the Poor House in 19th century England, so that further offspring would be prevented; Professor Boulding advocates marketable licenses for babies,* and Martha Willing advocates compulsory sterilization.† In a spasm of consistency quite untypical for the population controllers, she also raises the question why diabetics should be allowed to expand their numbers when, in a disruptive natural or unnatural disaster, "this vulnerable population" would not make it anyway.†

And this is as far as I will trespass into the field of mass psychology. The above remarks and suggestions are meant to be no more than food for thought, and perhaps an exhortation to more qualified writers to investigate the deeper psychological roots of the ecocult.

We will now turn to more tangible matters.

---

* *The Meaning of the 20th Century*, Harper & Row, New York, 1964.
†*Beyond Conception*, Gambit, Boston, Mass.

2

The Population Exploders

But suddenly our citizens were faced with nearly 200,000 corpses... The population was terrorized as TV screens became filled with scenes of horror from the disaster areas. Especially vivid was NBC's coverage of hundreds of people choking out their lives outside of New York's hospitals... Suddenly the United States discovered that it had a national consensus: population control was the only salvation...

A pretty grim scenario. Unfortunately, we're a long way into it already... Most of the people who are going to die in the greatest cataclysm in the history of man have already been born. More than three and a half billion people already populate our moribund globe...

Paul Ehrlich, *Eco-Catastrophe!* Ramparts Magazine, September 1969.

Not only the local ZPG organization and the hostess of last night's cocktail party, but reputable scientists assure us that population growth in the United States is exponentially exploding and unless checked, catastrophe must inevitably follow long before there is "standing room only." Who would dare to contradict these droves of learned men?

The facts would dare.

• The total fertility rate (children per woman) has been declining from a high of 3.7 in 1958 to an all-time low of 2.145 in May 1972, almost equal to the critical value of 2.11 corresponding to zero population growth.

• The total fertility rate continues to decline and is expected to drop within two or three years below the value 1.9, where present rates of immigration would be insufficient to compensate for the decline of the native population.

• The population density of the United States has not reached, and in all probability never will reach, as much as *one half* of the population densities in England, Germany, the Low Countries, Denmark, Italy, Hungary, Czechoslovakia or Poland. It is well below most of the rest of Europe.

• According to the latest figures released by the US Bureau of the Census (May 1972), the birth rate is down to an all-time low of 15.8; present trends indicate that the population of the United States will level off, probably below 260 million, some time before 2020, that is, in the generation of present teenagers.

EVERY year Malthus is proven wrong and buried — only to spring back to life again before the year is out, says the editor of an anthology rather partial to his ideas. For those who find such statements impressive, I have an equally impressive argument: Every year Malthus springs back to life — only to be proven wrong and buried again before the year is out.

The books that everybody admires are the books that nobody reads, said Anatole France, and I suspect that if more people read Malthus, they would admire him less. What did Malthus say? This, for example:

"Population, when unchecked, increases in geometrical ratio. Subsistence increases only in arithmetical ratio. A slight acquaintance with numbers will show the immensity of the first power compared of the second." (*An Essay on the Principle of Population*, 1798. The first and second powers evidently mean former and latter powers.)

Now the acquaintance with numbers of this contemporary of Gauss, Laplace and Lagrange must have been less than slight, or he would have heard of other progressions than arithmetical and geometrical. It is, of course, a cheap thing to deride the algebra of a curate who wrote some 170 years ago; but this is not my point. I note this, because today's instant demographers exhibit a similar ignorance of mathematics, and with less excuse than was the case for Malthus. What is more, today's instant demographers and computerized soothsayers make their assumptions with the same arbitrariness as Malthus did.

"I said that population, when unchecked, increased in a geometrical ratio, and subsistence for man in an arithmetical ratio," says Malthus, "let us examine whether this position be just.

"I think it will be allowed that no state has hitherto existed (at least that we have any account of) where the manners were so pure and simple, and the means of subsistence so abundant, that no check whatever has existed to early marriages, among the lower classes..." What does that have to do with the geometrical ratio?

"Whether the law of marriage be instituted or not, the dictate of nature and virtue..." The geometrical ratio, Malthus, the geometrical ratio!

"In a state therefore of great equality and virtue, where pure and simple manners prevailed..." Yes, yes, but what about the geometrical ratio?

"In the United States of America, where the means of subsistence have been more ample, the manners of the people more pure, and consequently the checks to early marriages fewer than in any of the modern states of Europe, the population has been found to double itself in twenty-five years." This was not yet the America of Billy the Kid or Al Capone, so let us not argue about the pure manners, but what about the geometrical ratio?

"This ratio of increase, though short of the utmost power of population, we will take as our rule, and say, that population, when unchecked, goes on doubling itself every twenty-five years in a geometrical ratio."

In other words, the talk about vice and virtue has nothing to do with it; the ratio is geometrical because Malthus so decreed it. Another writer might have asked whether the population increase of the United States in Malthus' time was primarily due to immigration or to reproduction, and as for the yardstick of 25 years, the makers of the two, click, two mints in one might have asked if it doubled once, will it double again? But no such questions are asked by the dean of the super-simplifiers. His reasoning for the arithmetic (linear) increase of food production is equally flimsy. In twenty-five years, he says, Britain's food production cannot be more than doubled. "The most enthusiastic speculator cannot suppose a greater increase than this." And that is all he needs to assert "Yet this ratio is evidently arithmetical. It may be fairly said, therefore, that the means of subsistence increase in arithmetical ratio."

Quod erat demonstrandum. But I will say this for Malthus. Although his reasoning is flimsy and totally unacceptable in any form other than a postulate, he at least informs us what his postulates are. Not as much can be said for the authors of *The Limits to Growth,* the computer study sponsored by the Club of Rome. The non-linear relationships used in that study, which are the crucial ones for determining the collapse of any system, are explicitly given in the case of only three examples, though the total number of casual relationships is "a hundred or so." The actual programs are not given in the book, and to my knowledge, have yet to be published.

It is not easy to predict future trends of a process whose course is known up to the present, particularly if the range within which the prediction will come true with a reasonable probability is to be narrow. In the case of population predictions this is just a little easier than in other cases, because of the long delay between cause and effect; we have a pretty good idea, for example, of the number of fertile women 16 years hence, because the increase will primarily be caused by those who are already alive as babies today, and because the decrease will primarily be caused (in America) by the natural transition to the non-fertile age rather than by death. Even so, the calculation of the trend is not as simple as that of compound interest, which is invariably thrown at us as the terrifying example of exponential growth by the doomsday prophets.

The fact that in some parts of the world population growth can numerically be roughly approximated by an exponential curve is not much help, for any curve whose slope is steadily increasing (or steadily decreasing) can be more or less satisfactorily approximated by *some* exponential curve, and whilst this is sometimes useful for numerical approximations, it does not give much insight into what is going on. In the United States, the slope of the population growth curve has no such properties, and it cannot be satisfactorily approximated by an exponential curve at all.

Exponential growth or — never considered by the doomsday prophets — exponential decrease is a process in which the (positive or negative) increment during any minute interval of time is proportional to the value of the variable at that time. If the constant of proportionality is positive, the resulting growth is very rapid; if it is negative, the resulting decrease is very rapid. In the case of a population that is not subject to immigration or emigration, the increment during a short interval equals the difference between births and deaths during that interval, which can be expressed as the difference between the birth and death rates (the number of births and deaths, respectively, per 1000 population). The resulting population growth or decline can therefore be exponential only in the special case that this difference is the same at all times (or the constant of proportionality would not be a constant).

But this is not the case. Both birth rates and death rates exhibit significant fluctuations, and only rarely do they fluctuate in harmony so as to keep the difference constant. There is, in fact, no immediate link between the two, and what links there may be, are complex, delayed, and often not yet sufficiently understood. Moreover, the difference between birth and death rates, far from being constant, is also insufficient to characterize population growth by itself. For example, reducing the infant mortality and prolonging the life span in old age will both reduce the death rate; but obviously increasing the non-fertile part of the population will lead to less growth than increasing the number of those who will eventually reproduce.

Obviously, then, population growth is not quite the same thing as money in a bank. Professional demographers therefore calculate population growth and its projection by a very different approach than a simplistic method which leads to an exponential. It requires some advanced mathematics, but it is not my purpose to scare the reader with stochastic processes and generating functions. Suffice it to say that the theory used by demographers yields an exponential only in one highly idealized special case.

But that is not the main point. The two points that are much more important than the mathematical details of population growth are the following. First, every sane man must concede that population growth cannot go on for ever; but that does not settle the question whether population finally stabilizes by a natural process (as it is now doing in the industrialized countries) or by catastrophe as the doomsday prophets assure us. When they are waving the bogeys of compound interest, wheat grains on a chess board and water lilies on a pond, they are merely side-stepping this question. Second, demographers, who unlike the doomsday prophets are familiar with the mathematics of population growth, project very carefully, tentatively and only for a few decades; even so, they have often been wrong because the projection always involves guesses at intangibles that are as yet little understood. In the past two decades, their estimates proved to be consistently too high and had to be revised downward several times. However, their estimates had nothing in common with the methods of the population exploder, who regards every rising curve as part of an exponential and projects it by means of a French ruler into the next 50 or 100 years in one lavish sweep of the megalomaniac.

Many demographers have spent their lives analysing the meaning of population statistics, and many aspects of population growth are still poorly understood. To give but one example, the fluctuations of birth rates and fertility rates are popularly thought to be strongly affected by wars and economic slumps, but demographers have not been able to find consistent relations, or even tendencies, tying changes in birth and fertility rates to social and economic upheavals. For example, the low of the US fertility rate in 1936 cannot be self-evidently ascribed to the great depression as is done by the Ehrlichs. For one thing, the downward trend started in the boom year of 1921; for another, that record was broken in the affluence of 1972.

Even the mere description of what is happening, without searching for deeper explanations, can often be deceptive. A statistic is, almost by definition, a numerical indicator resulting from a reduction of available information. For example, an average is a number calculated from a lot of other numbers which contained much more information than the reduced information carried by the average. A man who makes an average of $1,000 a month may be an employee with a steady salary or he may be a gambler who makes a few million in one month and loses a few in the next; the average has blotted out that information. A single statistic is therefore, more often than not, misleading, because it can never tell the whole story. On the other hand, the whole story (of population) is contained in vast quantities of birth and death registrations, census sheets, magnetic tapes and punched cards, and that is not much use without data reduction, either.

However, when a large number of important statistics points significantly in a certain direction, the situation becomes much clearer, and there is little doubt about what is going on. In economics, for example, there is often much argument among economists, businessmen and statisticians how certain indicators should be interpreted. But if unemployment is up, production is down, sales and profits are down, productivity is down, inventories are up, liquidities are down, cash flow is down, and stocks are down, then everybody knows that the economy is in a bad way, and that conviction is not altered by prices and wages which keep on rising in contradiction to old theories, nor by assurances of game plans and corners that are just about to be turned.

The same is true for population statistics. When all important indicators confirm the same trend, there is little doubt of what is happening, and alarmist shrieks of doomsday lose their credibility. The trend of US population is now, and has been for many years, in such a phase of little doubt where the indicators are pointing. Far

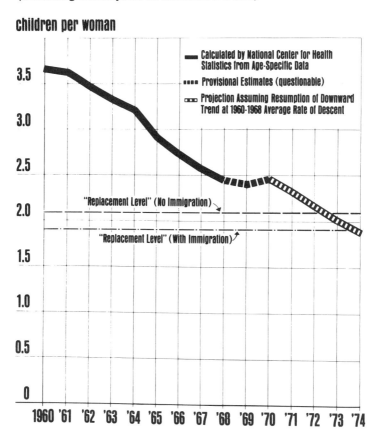

Figure 5—Trend in "Total Fertility Rate" 1960-1968, with Provisional 1969-1970 Estimates, Plus Projection to 1974 (assuming resumption of downward trend)

children per woman

Calculated by National Center for Health Statistics from Age-Specific Data

Provisional Estimates (questionable)

Projection Assuming Resumption of Downward Trend at 1960-1968 Average Rate of Descent

"Replacement Level" (No Immigration)

"Replacement Level" (With Immigration)

1960 '61 '62 '63 '64 '65 '66 '67 '68 '69 '70 '71 '72 '73 '74

The declining US fertility rate. From George Grier, *The Baby Bust* (see first footnote on p.46), reproduced by kind permission of The Washington Center for Metropolitan Studies. Since Grier's study was published, the fertility rate has been following the projected line shown above. The crossing of the replacement level of 2.11 was announced in May 1972.

from indicating a population explosion, these indicators are begin-ing to raise serious questions on the effects of a sudden stabilization and eventual *decline* of the population. There are several such effects, but among the detrimental effects that the population fanatics and eco-amateurs have never taken into consideration is the possibility of increased pollution through decline of the population. This is not a misprint, and I repeat it in italics: *increased pollution through decline of the population.* This possibility will be discussed in a moment. Moreover, such detrimental effects are not entirely depen-dent on whether this or that speculation comes true; if the US population, through some totally unforeseen quirk started to explode tomorrow, it could never undo what is already an established fact: There is a significant notch in the present age profile of the popula-tion. It now extends from age 11 downward, and deepens as it ap-proaches age zero. Unless someone immediately invents the birth of twelve-year old babies, that notch in the native population is here to stay for half a century, though, of course, it will move to higher age brackets as the present population ages.

These facts are well konown to demographers, though, like the engineers, they seem to have done little shouting in a world in-creasingly obsessed by the ecocult. But the necessary information is freely available to anyone seriously interested; all college libraries have the *Current Population Reports* issued by the U.S. Bureau of the Census. For the latest available information, one should consult the *Monthly Vital Statistics Reports* issued by the National Center for Health Statistics, Washington, D.C.

There is, incidentally, another interesting item connected with the *Current Population Reports.* The population projections issued by the U.S. Bureau of the Census are, like all projections, unreliable and dependent on the assumptions made in working out the projec-tion, in this case, on the uncertainty of future birth rates. The U.S. Bureau of the Census therefore used to issue four series of pro-jections (Series A, B, C, D), corresponding to different fertility as-sumptions. Thus, series B assumes that the completed fertility of women, i.e., the average number of children per 1,000 women at the end of childbearing, moves toward the level 3,100; for series C, this level is 2,775, and for Series D, it is 2,450. But by 1970, it became evident that all four series had proved too high, and the Bureau added a fifth series, E, corresponding to 2,110, or stabilization at zero population growth. That was a mere two years ago, and at that time, many experts regarded this series as unrealistically low; yet by May 1972, the fertility was down to 2,145.

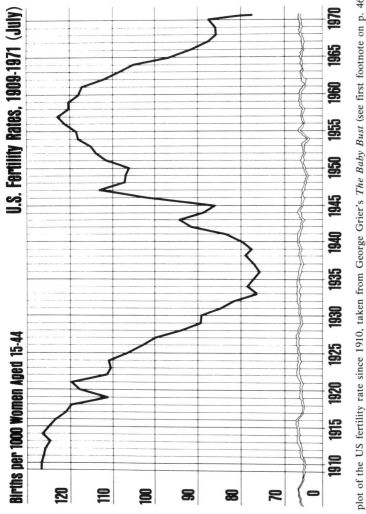

A plot of the US fertility rate since 1910, taken from George Grier's *The Baby Bust* (see first footnote on p. 46), reproduced by kind permission of the Washington Center for Metropolitan Studies. Since Grier's report was published, the fertility rate has dropped below the 1936 low, and is now lower than at any time in US history. Note also the previous decline in fertility rate, which started in 1921, and can therefore not be attributed to the Great Depression. Neither can the present decline be attributed to ZPG propaganda, which started in the late sixties.

I do not know whether the U.S. Bureau of the Census will find it necessary to begin issuing a Series F, corresponding to still lower fertilities, i.e., to population decline. But of one thing I feel fairly certain. If Series F does come into being, it will go to press simultaneously with some book called *Standing Room Only* or *A Kingdom for a Closet* or a new edition of Ehrlich's *Population Bomb*.

Let us now take a closer look at the pattern that emerges from some of the statistics.

All indicators of fertility (total, general, crude, age-specific, completed) have been declining for more than a decade. The total fertility rate, which demographers generally consider the most significant indicator of fertility, is down to 2.145, very close to 2.110, the value corresponding to zero population growth. (The total fertility rate is the number of children per 1,000 women, if each woman bears children at the age-specific rates prevailing at the given time, during each year of her life.) If the decline in fertility continues at the rate of the decade 1960-1970, then within a year or two the value 1.9 will have been reached; this corresponds to zero population growth even when compensation by immigration at present levels is taken into account. A further decline along the trend of the last 13 years will result in the decline of the total population of the United States some time after the year 2020, even taking into account immigration from foreign countries at the present rate.

All age-specific fertility rates have also been declining for the last 13 years. Until 1968, older women reduced their fertility level more rapidly than younger women. Since 1968, This characteristic no longer appears to hold, though it is too early to say whether this is a permanent new trend. The phenomenon is widely attributed to increased availability of contraceptives and abortion. If this phenomenon proves permanent, the decline in fertility may be accelerated. If increased ease of birth control proves to be its cause, the decline will presumably be even further accelerated by such advances as the "morning after pill." Whatever the reasons, if this trend should prove permanent, then the zero growth point for the US population will arrive earlier, and the subsequent decline will proceed faster than has been considered above.

The "second baby boom," predicted for the time when the babies of the post-World War II baby boom reached the age of parenthood, has so far failed to materialize, and with each passing year, the chances for such a boom are getting slimmer.

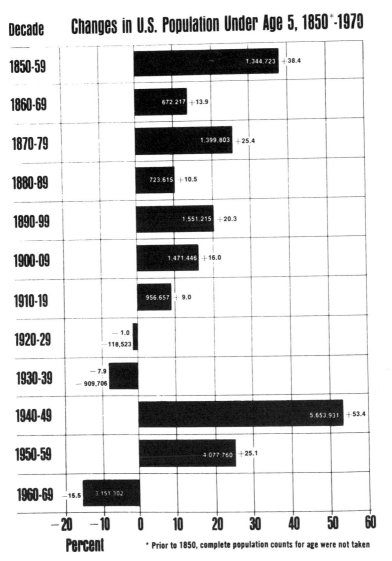

Decade   **Changes in U.S. Population Under Age 5, 1850*-1970**

Decade	
1850-59	1,344,723 +38.4
1860-69	672,217 +13.9
1870-79	1,399,803 +25.4
1880-89	723,615 +10.5
1890-99	1,551,215 +20.3
1900-09	1,471,446 +16.0
1910-19	956,657 +9.0
1920-29	−1.0 −118,523
1930-39	−7.9 −909,706
1940-49	5,653,931 +53.4
1950-59	4,077,760 +25.1
1960-69	−15.5 3,151,302

−20   −10   0   10   20   30   40   50   60

Percent   * Prior to 1850, complete population counts for age were not taken

The biggest decline in the pre-school age population in the history of US population statistics - the decade 1960-69. From George Grier's *The Baby Bust* (see first footnote on p. 46), reproduced by kind permission of the Washington Center for Metropolitan Studies. Whilst the decline has caused problems such as a surplus of teachers, the population exploders continue their talk about dependency ratios and overpopulation as the cause of insufficient funds for schools.

It should be noted, however, that whilst we are now very close to ZPG *fertilities*, this does not mean that the population has stopped growing. There is, for obvious reasons, a delay between fertility rates and growth rates. If the present fertility rates are maintained, the US population will stabilize at about 260 million in about 2030. If the present trend of decreasing fertilities continues, that point will come earlier, and the population will go into decline.

The number of deaths has increased since 1940, and it has been steadily increasing since 1954, though the increase is slow (from about 1.4 million deaths in 1940 to about 1.9 million in 1970). The considerable increase in life expectancy due to medical advances has not compensated for the increased number of deaths in an increasing population. With more people due to reach old age than ever before, the number of deaths is due to increase at an accelerated rate in the coming decades.

The death rate in future years can be predicted fairly accurately, because the people who must eventually die can already be counted; the uncertainty involves only the times at which they will die. However, there is no uncertainty of any kind involved in the numbers of the pre-school population. It is already here and it is the clue to the future population. And here we have a striking phenomenon, which is well known to demographers, but is ignored with blatant bias by the population exploders: The pre-school population (under 5 years) of the U.S. has declined by a totally unprecedented amount of 15.5% in the decade 1960-1969. A decline of the pre-school population has occurred only in two decades of US history of recorded statistics: In the decade 1920-29, when it declined by only one percent, and in the decade 1930-39, when it declined by less than 8%. A decline as spectacular as the one for the decade 1960-69 has not been recorded before; it is almost double of the previous record.

This point about the pre-school population is particularly important. It is this notch in the age profile which is an accomplished fact, not subject to speculations about the future. The age profile of a steadily increasing population must be wedge-shaped as shown in the figure opposite this page; there must be more young people than older ones, because there must be more children than parents. For a ZPG population, the profile must be more or less smooth (except for the top end, as people die at different ages), and for a declining population, the wedge is reversed, since there are more parents than children.

The 1969 age profile of the US population is shown in the figure on the opposite page. The US age profile used to be the wedge of an

Figure 10—A steadily growing population has an age profile like a pyramid ▲
A "ZPG" population will produce a roughly straight-sided profile ▦

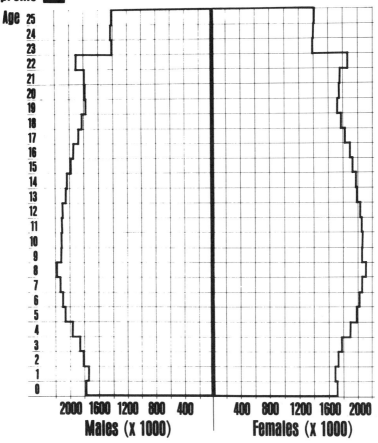

US age profile in 1969. From George Grier's *The Baby Bust* (see first footnote on p. 46), reproduced by kind permission of the Washington Center for Metropolitan Studies. The very slight increase at age zero has proved to be sporadic, and the taper now continues downward. A taper or deepening notch is visible in the figure from age 8 downward. Since then, age 8 has moved up to age 11, and the taper continues to (present, 1972) age zero. Whatever happens in the future, this notch will remain in the US age profile for some 50 years.

increasing population. In the last two decades, it first approached that of a ZPG profile, but the increasingly deepening notch from age 8 downward is plainly visible in the 1969 profile. The very slight increase of the profile at age zero (in 1969) proved to be sporadic, and the data published since then confirm the continued deepening of the notch which could be the wide end of the reversed wedge characterizing a *declining* population rather than the straight edge of a ZPG profile.

In fact, a person with the mentality of a population nut, who needs only two points for the unique interpolation of a figure eight, would swear high and low that this *is* the thick end of the wedge for the coming decline in the US population. But let us not answer soothsaying with soothsaying and oversimplification with oversimplification. No one knows for sure how the profile will continue. Its present shape only shows that a population explosion is nowhere in sight.

Similarly, the fact that the estimates of population growth by the demography experts have been consistently too high and that the date when ZPG would be achieved had to be revised downward several times (from an initial year 2,200 down to 2010) does not necessarily mean that it will have to be revised downward again. There are too many intangibles involved in attempts to predict accurately. There are, for example, some components of the US death rate which are apallingly high in comparison with other countries, and these could change if people become sufficiently determined about them. They are the following components: infant mortality, homicides, lack of industrial safety and automobile fatalities. The US infant mortality is higher than that in 20 other countries, and almost twice as high as that of Sweden or the Netherlands; this is mainly a social problem, since the infant mortality is twice as high among non-whites as among whites. Automobile fatalities, the number one killer of adults under 25, have cost more lives than all wars fought by America since the invention of the automobile. Homicides, the number two killer of persons between 15 and 24, have assumed gigantic proportions: The number of murders in New York City in 1970 was greater than the combined total for Britain, the Netherlands, Ireland, Switzerland, Spain, Sweden, Denmark and Norway; and more murders per year are commited in Houston, Texas, than in all of Britain. Perhaps future generations will find it hard to believe that in a country where a licence is required to sell pop corn, virtually anyone may own a hand gun (or an antitank gun, for that matter). "Gun control won't stop criminals" is a halftruth. Of course it won't; but it will stop the jealous girl friend, and the home owner who heard a noise in the garden, and the man who thinks the dealer cheated him, and the teenager who does not like his teacher. A knife takes courage, and poison takes time. A gun needs neither; it does not even allow anger to cool down.

However that may be, the fact is that the vast majority of Americans die in bed, and no radical changes can be expected from a change in the death rate if something should be done about gun control.

Another factor that should not be oversimplified is change in regional population due to migration rather than reproduction. Forces more powerful than ZPG propaganda are at work here. People want to move to where life is better, and in America they still have that most precious of all rights. Millions migrated to California; now California has almost 20 million inhabitants, the great majority of whom are populating a narrow strip between the sea and the desert. Naturally, the quality of life has decreased in that narrow strip, and the inexorable forces of equilibrium are driving people out again; the population of California is now on the decrease.

Such natural forces have a way of ultimately achieving something like an optimum balance of population distribution; but the people who are moving to where they think life is better often run into strong opposition. Who would oppose this natural process? The ZPG fanatics. Boulder, Colorado, is located in a very lovely spot, and its population has doubled in the last 20 years. The local ZPG organization, many (perhaps most) of whom arrived only recently, would deny others the same right of which its members availed themselves; their philosophy amounts, in effect, to saying "We made it; now let's see to it that nobody else makes it." A proposal to limit the city to 100,000 inhabitants by charter amendment was only narrowly defeated in the 1970 elections, and many people expect the proposal to pass when it is put on the ballot again. Such an amendment will probably prove unenforceable (what happens if citizen no. 100,000 gets pregnant?) and self-defeating (the city will be ringed by other cities), but there are even graver aspects to such a policy. The freedom of movement is perhaps the most precious of all freedoms; for example, many people in the Soviet colonies believe that if a country has no freedom of speech, press or assembly and no due process under the law, it should at least allow its citizens to get the hell out of there. This may seem utterly irrelevant to a policy with the innocent name "planned population growth," but a flame can arise from a spark. Making laws denying people rights reserved only to the lawmaker, and forbidding them to settle on land that does not belong to them, is a beginning; what is the end?

THE last few paragraphs dealt with secondary ramifications of the population pattern. Now let us return to its essence, which is that no population explosion in the United States is anywhere in sight and that much more probably, the population will go into decline during the life time of the generation now in their teens. Detailed information on all of the assertions made in the preceding pages is as far as the nearest library, or wherever else the reports of the U.S. Bureau of the Census can be found. A particularly lucid report on the population patterns of the last two decades should also be mentioned: *The Baby Bust* by George Grier,* a short report full of facts and figures. Its author has no ax to grind, and he presents the facts with the cool objectivity of the professional demographer. Parts of the preceding discussion are based on the information contained in Grier's report, but anyone seriously interested in the question should obtain the original.

What does the ZPG movement have to say about these facts published by the U.S. Bureau of the Census and the National Center for Health Statistics?

Very little. Let us not waste time on the zealots who advocate compulsory sterilization and discourage treatment of diabetics,† but let us take a look at some authors and bodies from whom one would expect more responsibility.

The final (1972) report of the Colorado Environmental Commission, a body appointed by the Governor and General Assembly of the state, for example, continues to beat the drum of the old bogeys, the population sections (and some others) of the report periodically referring to the works of Paul Ehrlich. The report does state that the total fertility rate has declined from a peak of 3.69 in 1959-61 (this may be a minor error — the rate peaked earlier) to 2.2 in 1971, but this is not in the bold print of the report and mentioned only once, whereas the idea of threatening disaster by overpopulation is driven home by constant repetition. Samples of the bold print look like this:

* George Grier, *The Baby Bust*, Washington Center for Metropolitan Studies (1717 Massachusetts Ave., N.W., Washington, DC 20036), 1971; $2.50.

† For a very illuminating report on these humanitarians, see Samuel McCracken, *The Population Controllers*, Commentary, vol. 53, no. 5, pp. 45-52, May 1972. Available as a reprint from Commentary Reports, 165 East 56th St., New York, NY 10022.

"Zero population growth is an inescapable fact. The only question is when and how. Do we take steps now to set population goals and establish programs to limit our population growth voluntarily, or do we wait for natural methods to achieve zero growth? The former can lead to a quality life; the latter can only lead to disaster." The passage is repeated almost verbatim elsewhere in the report, and lest anyone take the word *disaster* metaphorically, it says "...or natural methods will bring about zero growth *by violent means* while we wait" (my italics). Heavy doses of legislation pertaining to population control are recommended: the enacting of a state population policy, including the establishment of a council of population advisors; legislative limitations on the growth of metropolitan areas; the enacting of "all possible" legislative incentives to birth-rate reduction, including monetary incentives for sterilization and tax incentives for small families; funding of all aspects of fertility control. The latter recommendation is accompanied by the bold print warning "Whether the next generation opts for two or three children may well decide the course of history. . ."

There is also the argument which goes beyond the usual population hysterics, and which can once again be traced back to Paul Ehrlich. The report says "This population explosion may very well be the foremost threat to the future of mankind, the most likely to trigger a nuclear holocaust." This is indeed news. Not a handful of ruthless fanatics in the Kremlin, the biggest concentration of power known to history, may trigger a nuclear holocaust, but the population explosion in countries that have not yet learned to produce toothpicks, let alone nuclear missiles. And the answer to this threat is decreasing the birth rate and monetary incentives for sterilization in Colorado. One might offer the population controllers a new slogan: National Security through National Sterilization.

There may indeed be reasons to worry about rapid population growth in Colorado, where the most important factor is not the birth rate, but immigration, and where water resources are not particularly plentiful. Then again, such worries may be groundless. But who is going to take the arguments against population growth in Colorado seriously if they are accompanied by threats of nuclear holocaust and recommendations for tax incentives for sterilization?

But apparently nuclear holocaust is not the only thing that threatens Colorado if it keeps its doors open to new arrivals or if birth control is not practiced with sufficient zeal. "Colorado's 104,247 square miles are not finite," says the report in the section on Population Planning and Policy. It is true that some of Colorado's area is taken up by the Continental Divide and the adjacent mountain ranges of the Rockies, whose splendor should surely be preserved. But to use 104,247 square miles as an argument against population growth is like complaining that there is too little coffee in Brazil. The area of Colorado is greater than that of Great Britain and Northern Ireland, and almost half of that of France. It is now populated by less than 3 million people. Accepting the Commission's assumption that Colorado doubles its population every 30.1 years, it would take more than one and a half centuries before the population density approached even the present population density of Great Britain (large parts of which are also mountainous, and the population density therefore very uneven); but again using the Commission's assumption of present trends, this could be achieved only by herding no less than one quarter of the entire US population into Colorado.

How do such biased attitudes get into an official report? I cannot say. The lady who chaired the Committee on Population and Related Problems of the commission is listed, as President, Colorado Institute on Population Problems, Englewood. I found no such institute listed in the telephone directory of the Denver metropolitan area (from which it does not follow that it must necessarily be inferior). The other members of the committee were a State Senator, a State Representative, a businessman, a newspaper publisher, and four engineers, but apparently no professional demographers. I have little doubt that the members of the committee have been exposed to the population bogeys like everyone else. Like many others, they may have read Ehrlich's *Population Bomb*. It seems less probable that they have studied the reports issued by the U.S. Bureau of the Census. If not, it is not surprising that they should simply accept conventional wisdom.

What about Paul Ehrlich himself, the man the above report refers to, and who is often considered the founder of the ZPG movement? Does he not know the US population statistics for the last decade and more? He knows some of them, but dismisses them very casually; and he simply ignores others in his latest book. In *Population, Resources, Environment* (1970) by Paul R. and Ann H. Ehrlich, the authors say "The fertility rate *has* been on a downward trend, but the 1968 fertility rate of about 85 was still higher than the lows reached during the depression (when it was well below 80)." This reminds me of the man who fell from the 20th floor of a skyscraper, and falling past the 2nd floor said "So far, so good." In the two years since the Ehrlichs' book was published, their argument has, of course, been punctured, for the fertility rate has now descended beyond the low of the depression (which probably had little to do with the depression, for the decline started in 1921 and reached a low in 1936). But I have no doubt that Dr. Ehrlich has meanwhile thought up equally profound arguments, for the book is full of speculations of what *might* happen (the polar ice caps might melt, for example*) and why anything but a population explosion is not feasible. The authors dismiss the sharp and consistent fertility decline of more than a decade by the statement "The optimists who greeted the decline in birth rates in the 1960's with pronouncements about the end of the population explosion would probably interpret a December thaw as a sign of spring."

Of course, the Ehrlichs might be right, for all I know (and for all they know); fertility rates might start to climb again tomorrow. But what about the deepening notch in the *present* US age profile, which will remain with us for some 50 years? The Ehrlichs do give an age profile of the US population: It was 10 years old when the book was published, and the only comment the authors saw fit to make was that the "large bulge in the 0-14 age class represents the age group that will be reproducing in the 1970's." That was the bulge that moved up to the 9 to 23 class in 1969 (see figure on p. 43), and that has now moved up another two years to the 11 to 25 class. And the deepening notch appearing in the profile that has appeared in the last 12 years? I have found no mention of this in the section on age structure, in the chapter on population structure and projection, nor anywhere else in this book on population and related matters.

How about the fact that the drop in the pre-school age population is the largest in US history? The Ehrlichs pay it the same attention and make the same comments: none. Perhaps this is a December thaw, too; a December thaw that will last at least half a century.

In *The Population Bomb*, Paul Ehrlich threatened mainly by the population explosion; in the book mentioned above, the Ehrlichs have interwoven this theme with several more bugaboos based on equally strong evidence. I must confess at this point that I am galled by the Ehrlichs more than by many other doomsday prophets, and the reason is their wanton use of the Second Law of Thermodynamics. It is not just that their presentation of the Second Law will

---

* The statement introducing this and similar speculations reads verbatim: "It is worthwhile to consider some of the climatic changes that *might* occur." (Italics by the Ehrlichs.) P. 147 of the mentioned book, W.H. Freeman &Co., San Francisco, 1970.

make any physicist wince: "Since the second law says that the *overall* tendency of all processes is ... *away* from high temperature, it is saying that, overall, more and more energy is becoming less and less usable. Typically, the manifestation of this degradation of energy is the production of heat at relatively low, hence useless, temperatures — for example, the heat of a car's exhaust, the heat of tire friction against the road, the heat radiated by your body, the heat of a decomposing animal carcass." What infuriates me in this travesty of the Second Law of Thermodynamics is what infuriates people most often: There is a kernel of truth in this almost totally unrecognizable carricature.

What the Ehrlichs appear to be referring to is the so-called Thermal Death of the Universe; they do not use that name, but they do say that the laws of thermodynamics "make it clear that all the energy used on the face of the earth, whether of solar or nuclear origin, will ultimately be degraded to heat."   That is where the kernel of truth is. What the Second Law of Thermodynamics says in its most often used formulation is that energy must be expended to make heat flow from a cooler body to a warmer one. From this and the First Law (which amounts to the conservation of energy) it can be shown that in every energy conversion there is a fraction of energy that is irreversibly converted to heat, but that has little to do with the tales quoted above. Unbeknownst to the Ehrlichs, some of the heat of a car exhaust can be converted into non-thermal energy, and snakes, reptiles and fish do work against friction and gravity at the "low, hence useless" temperature of a decomposing animal carcass. The kernel of truth is that in every energy conversion, some fraction of the energy is irreversibly converted to heat. It does not follow that all the energy converted to heat must irreversibly be degraded. It does, however, follow that after *infinitely many* energy conversions within a *closed* system no form of energy other than heat can remain. In accordance with that theory, all of the universe will eventually have no form of energy other than heat, i.e., totally random motion of its molecules. Disregarding philosophical questions of whether the Second Law applies throughout the universe, and whether the universe is infinite or behaves as a closed system, let me only note that the Ehrlichs do not mention one little detail: As far as "Spaceship Earth" is concerned, a thermal death of all energy conversions can take place in an infinite time interval after the 10 to 100 billion years for which the Sun will still be pumping energy into the "spaceship."

Reading the Ehrlichs' book, I got the distinct impression that they do not fully understand what the Second Law is about, and this excuses them; for otherwise I would say that if a doomsday prophet has to resort to the Thermal Death of the Universe, he must be totally bankrupt of all scarecrows, bogeys and bugaboos.

THE ignorance of the population exploders is not limited to physics and demography; it extends to economics as well. Alas, I share their ignorance of economics; yet I believe I am not quite as blind to the basic facts. I am ignorant of the effects of mergers on the price of preferred stock; but I do know the basic economic difference between a band of apes or cave men and a civilization, and it is this: The per capita productivity of a civilization is such that its members, on the average, have the capability of producing more goods and services than they consume.

Apes and cavemen roamed the country hunting for food, of which they brought in as much as was necessary to sustain the tribe, or they perished; the productivity of the hunters was so low that they were unable to free other members of the tribe for writing books on population control. The Great Agricultural Revolution that began, in some parts of the world, 10,000 years ago, radically changed this situation: By raising crops and livestock, men so increased their productivity in food production that they were able to free a fraction of their population for the production of other goods and for the provision of other services. This excess productivity, the productivity in excess of what is needed for the bare minimum to keep the producer alive, has risen to immense values in the industrialized countries. The employees of general Motors produce vastly more cars than they drive, and the operators of a power station produce vastly more power in a minute than they consume in a lifetime; yet neither, strictly speaking, produces a necessity for bare subsistence, as the nuts in the communes living on worms seem bent on proving. But some of us still have the old-fashioned desire of driving a car and reading by electric light, and we obtain these luxuries by exchanging them for other goods or services that we produce. The bookkeeping of these exchanges is performed with the aid of money, salaries, taxation, and a hundred other means. Whether this system of bookkeeping is satisfactory is not the point here; the point is that high productivity enables us, however inequitably, to exchange goods and services other than only food and food production, protection from the elements by shelter and clothing, and whatever other goods and services are needed for barely staying alive.

But the activities for which the high productivity of society has freed the men and women engaged in the production of nonessential goods and services does not only include the writing, printing and publishing of books on population control; it also includes, if society so chooses, the prevention, suppression and removal of pollution. Please let me repeat that in italics: *It also includes the prevention, suppression and removal of pollution.*

More apes produce more excrement, agreed. But to say that more people produce more pollution is less than half the story: It is that part of the story on which the population controllers and computerized soothsayers have harped with stubborn exclusiveness and sleep-inducing monotony in book after book, lecture after lecture and computer program after computer program. The other part of the story is that more people can, if they choose to do so, produce more prevention and removal of pollution; by using high-productivity technology they can more than compensate for pollution; and *the more people, the greater this overcompensation* (at least up to a point, for no system can remain linear in an unbounded range).

Of course, it does not follow that merely because the excess productivity is *available* for cleaning up pollution that this productivity is used for that purpose. Indeed, contemporary America demonstrates that this is not so; the excess productivity beyond what is needed for mere survival is gigantic, but only a very small part of it is used to keep the environment clean. But merely because someone's carpet is dirty, even though he has plenty of vacuum cleaners, does it follow that "the more vacuum cleaners, the more dirt on the carpet"? The mere presence of vacuum cleaners does not guarantee a clean carpet; but the dirt on the carpet is harder to get rid of if there is a lack of them. A large population may not spend its economic resources prudently and may find itself in a polluted environment, but this is a consequence of imprudent housekeeping, not an inevitable byproduct of a large population. On the contrary, a small population will have bigger headaches with the housekeeping; the fact that fewer people require less electric power (for example) will not help, because the excess productivity of a population declines with its numbers; and though it is still true that the average man can clean up more dirt than he produces, a smaller population will be harder pressed on just how much of its excess productivity it should allot to clean-up.

This is one of the very basic points that has been consistently overlooked by the population controllers, reversionists and super-simplifiers. One such super-simplifier, for example, unblushingly put the following into print: "The facts of the case can be usefully summarized in a simple verbal formula:

$$(\text{Population}) \times (\text{Prosperity}) = (\text{Pollution})$$

where the word 'pollution' stands for congestion and other spirit-abrading phenomena as well."*

There are some questions the super-simplifiers never ask. What happens, to pollution or other factors, if zero population growth is approached too rapidly? What happens, to pollution or other factors, if the population goes into decline?

If someone's house is on fire, he does not usually scream for flood control; and if his house is threatened by rising floods, the first thing he tries to save is usually not the fire extinguisher. Unless, perhaps, he is a population control fanatic. With all the indicators pointing to zero population growth in the United States within the generation of present teenagers, with the pre-school age population already showing a deepening, unprecedented, and unremovable notch, what are the population exploders in the United States doing? They are screaming overpopulation, sterilization, abortion, pollution, pestilence, doomsday, holocaust and apocalypse; they are melting the polar ice caps and concocting new computer programs of suicide guaranteed under all conditions; they are raving against science and technology and cutting research budgets; they refuse to be misled by the facts.

But zero population growth is not a stable state; population does not return to a privileged state like a spring rebounds to its original position after being compressed or expanded. When population is stabilized, it merely has the property of zero change (or small fluc-value compared to positive or negative changes. A temporarily stabilized population may suddenly begin to grow very rapidly; it may also begin to die out very rapidly. Everyone must, by now, have heard the tales dramatizing the rapid growth of an exponential function or a divergent geometric series. But all these dramatic tales can be reversed to dramatize the rapid *de*crease of an exponential function or the terms of a convergent geometric series. For example: By doubling their number every day, it took water lilies one year to cover the surface of a pond; they then started to die and disappear at the same rate as they grew. How long before the pond is half

---

* G. Hardin, *Population, Pollution and Political Systems*, pp.59-68 of *Population, Environment and People*, ed. by Rene Dubos, McGraw-Hill, New York, 1971.

empty again? Answer: one day. Or: If all the wheat grains in the world could be piled onto the first square of a chess board, and half of them removed and piled onto the second square, and half of them removed and piled onto the next square, and so on, how many grains would be piled on the 64th square? Answer: None; there are not enough wheat grains in the world to last through 64 steps of this process.

Of course, as we have seen before, population is not the same thing as water liles, chess boards or compound interest, no matter whether it is increasing or declining. One of the many dissimilarities is the fact that a human population represents a system with a very long time constant. When a compressed spring is released, it will overshoot its equilibrium position and oscillate; but the oscillations will die out quickly and the spring will come to rest within a few seconds. In other systems, cause and effect do not follow each other immediately; even the very short delay between depressing the key of a large church organ and the perception of the intended musical tone is one of the reasons why an accomplished pianist may find playing a church organ extremely disconcerting, and sometimes impossible. In the case of population, cause and effect are delayed by the time elapsing between birth and fertility, or at least 16 years. The general criteria that make a system overshoot and oscillate rather than approach its ultimate state aperiodically (creepingly, without oscillations) have been the subject of intensive research, and they are now well known and understood. What is totally unknown is whether these criteria are satisfied in the case of population. We are, in this case, in the predicament of understanding systems theory, but not this specific system.

There are, nevertheless, certain features that we can predict with reasonable accuracy. And one of these is that if the population controllers' dreams came true and we were able to regulate population by compulsion, persuasion, legislation or any other such naive prescriptions with the same accuracy with which a housewife regulates the baking of an apple pie, then it would still take decades before the system even began to react, more decades before we were sure how the system behaved, and possibly centuries before the oscillations died out. Now suppose the people living at that time did not share Ehrlich's conviction that he knew what was good for them; what then? To drive a car where you have to turn the steering wheel *now* in order to cope with a curve that will come up in 20 years hence needs more than expertise in the Second Law of Thermodynamics. If the anticipated curve fails to materialize, your car will crash off the road, and it might take literally centuries to get it onto the right road again. But what is the "right" road? Not the road that the passengers consider right, but the road that was considered right by their great-grandfathers.

Here, then, is a legitimate case of asking "what if?" and of being wary of interfering with a natural process, two cherished concerns dear to every econut's heart. But apparently they must not be applied to legitimate cases. Yet there is, I believe, cause for concern. Samuel McCracken (see footnote on p. 46) has paraphrased the population controllers' simplistic slogans with a pungent counter-slogan: *Fewer People, Less Doing.* That sums up what has been pointed out above concerning productivity, apes and economics. What does it mean for pollution prevention and removal?

It means, first and foremost, more energy for cleaning up the present state of the environment, and more research for developing pollutionless energy sources. The environmentalists are howling that this is a vicious circle because more energy consumption creates more pollution; but this is the old argument about more vacuum cleaners making more dirt. Electric power can clean up more pollution than it creates. Even thermal power plants (let alone nuclear ones) can be used for the power needed to run sewage treatment plants, recycling operations, scrubbers, precipitators, and all other pollution removal equipment, and the pollution created even by power stations now in existence will demonstrably be far smaller than the amount removed. The only vicious circle is this: There are not enough power stations to satisfy the demand, in large part due to the environmental organizations who oppose power stations of any kind on the grounds that they pollute.

The energy crisis and the baseless assertion that the generation of power *must* pollute will be discussed in Chapter 4; here we are concerned with population questions. If the population goes into a decline within the coming four or five decades, who is going to clean up the environment? Who is going to prevent pollution? Who is going to man the power stations? Who is going to oppose the nuts who want to shut down the power stations on the grounds that pollution removal pollutes? "But less people will create less pollution," say the population controllers. Yes; but they will clean up even less of what they create, as has been discussed before. Less people provide less surplus services, and they will use them to stay alive, not to clean up. Less people will be powerless to clean up the present mess, let alone to prevent it from increasing. Less people will not have enough economic muscle to provide the investments in engineering skills and in physical plants which are needed to produce pollutionless cars. Less people will not be able to provide the funds for research and development for pollutionless power generation. Less people will drive in the old, polluting cars. Less people will, between brown-outs and black-outs, draw current from the old power stations belching millions of tons of pollutants into a grey sky. Perhaps not even that: Less people, all brainwashed to oppose technology, may eventually end up as another Soviet colony.

For a power station was made to generate power and a car was made to run; pollution is *not* a process essential to their operation. There is a natural law saying that conversion of energy must give rise to heat; there is no natural law saying that a power station must pollute. And indeed, it need not; as will be discussed in Chapter 4, there are several ways of totally pollutionless generation of electric power. But these methods will need more economic muscle, more research, more technology, and more people skilled in controlling it.And these methods are not opposed by imaginary devils who love only profits and pollution, but by the environmental fanatics, the technophobes and the population exploders.

If the population fanatics had their way, who would clean up Lake Erie? The three inhabitants of Detroit?

If I have pointed to the bleak possibilities of brown-outs and black-outs, to the prospects of more pollution, and even to that of a Soviet colony, I should not leave it at that, for doomsday prophecies do not cease to be simplistic when their algebraic sign is reversed. A decrease in population need not, in itself, lead to these gloomy prospects, particularly if the productivity and the technological sophistication of the population increases in proportion to, or in excess of, their declining numbers. Power stations can, and will, one day be manned by computers, and the threat of a country whose overstretched military economy can produce sputniks, but not pipe cleaners, can be defeated by superior technology controlled by a free and dedicated population. But this cannot be achieved by the simple recipe of zero population growth; that approach, combined with curbing technological progress, will guarantee only more of the evils the environmentalist and population controller seek to cure.

The sincerity of the population controllers may be the purest, and it is not their sincerity that I am attacking; but in the long run this sincerity is of interest only to the psychologist. We are talking not about good intentions, but about pollutants belched into the air by stacks made of hard concrete and measured in tons per day.

The population controller makes his unwitting contribution to pollution, though admittedly it is negligible to the far more blatant and effective contribution by the environmental fanatics and the technophobes, however unwitting their complicity may be. But at least the environmentalists and technophobes can point to their good intentions of keeping the air and water clean. Are the motives of the population controller equally noble? Just how noble is the philosophy of the man who says "I am here already; there is no room for the rest of you"?

I HAVE objected to the population controllers on the grounds that the facts of population growth in the United States contradict their premises and assertions, and I have so far attacked their fallacies only as they apply them to America. And with few exceptions, they do apply them to America, even if they invoke the underdeveloped countries in irrelevant attempts to make their point.

In the underdeveloped countries, particularly in South America and the Indian subcontinent, population growth does indeed present a different pattern than in the industrialized countries. Population growth is rapid there, and food production is still on a lamentably low level.But on reading the population control literature, the reader will find no discussion of *whether* anything can or should be done about this; instead, he will find the most heterogeneous, muddle-headed and offensively patronizing proposals, all of which have only one thing in common: They are totally unrealistic. These proposals also have another highly interesting property: They are abnormally slim in comparison to the very same authors' exhortations to act now, time is running out, how much longer are we going to play ostrich, and so forth. Typically, the greater part of the Ehrlichs' book is devoted to painting doomsday visions; of the 383 pages, only very few mention proposals how to stop population growth in the underdeveloped countries. Such proposals are, for example, briefly discussed in the section labeled "Involuntary Fertility Control." In the remaining pages, the underdeveloped countries are considered only in rather general terms, except for the proposal of triage, and the last section of the book, *Recommendations: A Positive Program* is concerned exclusively with handing out advice to Americans, particularly their government. ("Political pressure must be applied immediately to induce the United States government to assume its responsibility to halt the growth of the American population." — "A massive campaign must be launched ... to *de-develop the United States*." Italics by the Ehrlichs.) This is not untypical for the population controllers: They write a whole book of doomsday fantasies, on the lack of proteins in the diet of Peruvians, on the overcrowding in India, on the population explosion in Egypt, and after finding that there are too many other people in the world, they turn on the US government with angry demands to do more about sterilization in the U.S.A.

"Several coercive proposals deserve serious consideration," write the Ehrlichs in the section on involuntary fertility control, "mainly because we ultimately have to resort to them unless current trends in birth rates are rapidly reversed by other means. Some coercive measures are less repressive or discriminatory, in fact, than some of the socioeconomic measures that have been proposed." [*We* have to resort to coercive proposals. Who is *we*?] A number of such measures are then discussed, though the authors make it fairly clear that their sympathies lie with the "triage" proposal; they write that the Paddocks' book *Famine — 1975!*, in which this proposal is made, "will have to be adopted by world-wide policy planning groups," and they give the triage proposal sympathetic coverage in a special box.

In discussing compulsory fertility control, neither the Ehrlichs nor most others who know what is good for the underdeveloped countries have considered another question: What do the victims have to say about Bwana Econut with the big knife?

At present, they are not exactly putting out the welcome mat for him. They appear far more interested in taking the road that has virtually eliminated large families in the West: industrialization. America's poor have discerned the philosophy "We made it, now let's see to it that nobody else does," which often masquerades in the ecological cloak. Will no such thoughts appear in the minds of the peoples and governments of the underdeveloped countries? Is it any wonder if these people find it offensive to be lectured on the evils of prosperity and the need for sterilization by pundits in the industrialized countries with their heated swimming pools and electric toothbrushes? It is not the first story they have heard from the White Man; they cannot be expected to have forgotten that they used to be called chinks, goons and niggers. What can they be expected to think now when they are told about "Spaceship Earth"? Obviously, that the White Man travels first class on this ship, and that he is telling the others "There is too many of you."

Much as I dislike the Ehrlichs' attitudes, it would be foul play to convey the impression that they are racists; they are not, as must be amply evident to anyone who has read their book, and the books written by Paul Ehrlich alone, and I wish to stress this point for the reader who has not read the originals. But once again, I am less interested in good intentions, and more interested in the hard effects that they produce.

As long as the governments of the underdeveloped countries do not want compulsory fertility control, the proposal is totally unrealistic, and it would not be much more realistic if they could be persuaded to attempt it. A stick never works as well as a carrot under any circumstances; how, then, do you compel people to submit to something that many of them consider worse than death?

Besides, it is not the birth rate that is causing the population explosion in the underdeveloped countries. The evidence shows what one would expect from common sense — it has not substantially changed over the years. What has changed is the death rate and life expectancy, due to DDT, the arch-villain which conquered malaria, due to the Green Revolution, which gave the lie to predictions of worldwide famine in the late forties and fifties, due to penicillin and better medical care. A consistent population controller would therefore work on this end of the question, for morality is never a deterrent for the man who knows what is good for you. The population controllers do, indeed, realize this weakness of their crusade, and many of them apologize that family planning is "merely the first step." The first step to nowhere, for they have no second steps.

With some exceptions. There are some who have the guts to say what the second step is: Starve them to death. This is the proposal of the Paddock brothers,* who proposed the "triage procedure. The term comes from military medicine. When casualties in battle are so high that not all can be treated by the dressing station, they are divided into three groups: those who cannot be saved anyway, those who will somehow survive anyway (the "walking wounded") and those who will die only if denied immediate medical care. If merely a limited amount of medical care can be given, it is given only to the last group. The Paddocks apply this terminology to classify the countries to which American food aid should be given or denied. For

* W. and P. Paddock, *Famine — 1975!*, Little, Brown & Co., Boston and Toronto, 1967.

example, by the Paddocks' choice, India is in the "Can't be saved" category, Libya is a "Walking Wounded," and Pakistan should receive food.

Since morality has gone out the window anyway, one might ask why not write a book called *The Cannibal's Cookbook: How to Save Your Country from Overpopulation and Starvation with Knife and Fork [Respectively]*?

However, I do not wish to get involved in problems of morality, which is a very relative concept, and to some people, a very flexible one as well. A procedure based on the desire to save the maximum number of lives is hardly in itself immoral, though it is made glaringly evident that this is not the basis on which the Paddocks make their recommendations. Cold-blooded as the Paddocks' book may appear from this brief mention, it is written with more logic than most books on the population explosion, and it is certainly less hypocritical. But casting aside questions of morality, it is doubtful that the proposal is realistic. Could the American people be persuaded to support such a callous proposal? Perhaps they could, but I doubt that it would make much difference one way or the other.

For there is no reason to think that the underdeveloped countries will develop in substantially different ways than was the case for the West. On the contrary, there is evidence from Taiwan and other countries that the pattern is exactly the same. In Europe, too, the birth and fertility rates were high, and in some parts of Europe 15-children families were still not unfrequent in living memory. Only a century ago, it was quite usual for a woman to bear 12 or 15 children, though this number rarely survived. The population was kept in check by infant mortality, famine, disease, and war. As late as the 19th century, Ireland was ravished by famine. As late as the 18th century, famine killed well over 100,000 people in the small province of Bohemia (then a part of the Austrian Empire). The Thirty Years' War (1618-1648) is believed to have reduced the population of Central and Northern Europe by one half, and before that, entire cities and communities were depopulated by the plague. This must have been the golden age of the population nut.

But as economic patterns changed, so did population statistics. The peasants and the early industrial workers knew what many a population fanatic has forgotten: that a man produces more than he consumes. When a family lost a member, it lost a breadwinner (or a potential breadwinner), for even the starvation wages paid to the early industrial workers helped to keep their parents and other members of their families alive, and when the Shaftesbury Bill forbidding child labor was passed in England, the hardest hit were not the employers who employed 8 year old children (and even younger ones in the chnimney sweeping trade), but the families who needed their income. The situation changed as time went on; a man still produces more than he consumes, especially in a highly industrialized society, but he becomes a breadwinner only after he has completed his education, and he does not start to help feeding his family at the age of seven or eight, as he did in the early industrial revolution.

As industrial growth proceeded, and life became more livable, fertility rates plummeted, not by percentage points, but by factors of two, three, and more. The birth rate in Europe is now of the same order as that in the United States; it is somewhat higher in countries with comparatively little industry (Iceland, Ireland, Romania), and a little lower in some others (France, Germany, Belgium). Whilst it is possible to argue about the reasons that have produced the drastic drops in fertility as countries industrialized, there can be no reasonable doubt about the existence of the phenomenon itself. Nor is it limited to Europe. It occurred in America (though here the statistics are difficult to interpret due to the strong impact of immigration), and it occurred in Japan. A recent and dramatic example is Taiwan, where the birth rate dropped from 211 in 1951 to 149 in 1966,* a time span of only 16 years. This was, of course, also the time when Taiwan became industrialized.

Besides demonstrating the fact that population growth slows dramatically in industrialized societies, the history of population growth in Europe also demonstrates another point: the utter futility of incentives (let alone prohibitions) in attempting to regulate fertility. The totalitarian regimes offered, and offer, great rewards for large families. Neither Hitler's nor Mussolini's ravings about multiplying The Race produced a baby boom of any kind. Bonuses for children are offered in all parts of the Soviet Empire; not merely an income tax exemption, but a positive monthly bonus, which (in Russia itself, Czechoslovakia, and probably most other Soviet colonies) equals the tax withholdings with the birth of the fourth child, and becomes a net profit with the birth of a fifth. The effect: nil. You can brainwash a man into believing that Stalin was a kindhearted father of the people, but not into begetting a fifth child for a monthly bonus. The USSR, and many of its colonies, award titles such as "Meritous

---

* K. Davis, *Population Policy: Will Current Programs Succeed?* Science, vol. 158, pp.730-739 (1967).

Mother of the People" and "Hero of Socialist Motherhood." These titles are awarded with much ceremony to mothers of 10 or 12 children, but only the Hero of Socialist Motherhood and her husband know for sure what made them beget so many children, and under these conditions I can only ask for your advice. Would *you* have 10 or 12 children just so you or your wife could be awarded the proud title of Hero of Socialist Motherhood? Not even if they promised to have your photograph in in *Pravda*?

The many fringe benefits offered to families with many children (such as decent living quarters) have also had no effect. All incentives for more children have proved futile. The USSR has the same order of birth rate as other industrial countries (only slightly higher than the U.S.); the birth rate is slightly lower for Russians than for the non-Russian Soviet peoples, who are largely rural folk. The carrot has not worked for inducing people to have more children; why should it work to induce them to have less? If the carrot does not work, how can the stick?

Obviously, then, the solution to overpopulation in the underdeveloped countries is not Bwana Econut with the big knife, but industrialization. Until the underdeveloped countries are industrialized and reach a standard of living comparable to that of Europe, they will have the same high birth and fertility rates as Europe used to have. Population will be kept in check by much the same forces that kept the population in check in Europe before it was industrialized: famine, disease, poverty, squalor, ignorance, local wars. DDT can defeat the malaria-carrying mosquito, but it cannot defeat squalor and ignorance. Education without the forces and background of an industrialized society is little more than an empty word. I do not believe the white population fanatics can do much about that with their naive proposals. Industrialization will progressively cure the evils of famine, disease, poverty and excessive fertility, as it has cured them and is still curing them, ecohysterics to the contrary, in the industrialized countries.

Industrialization is also what the underdeveloped countries want above all themselves. Though this is a book of rebuttals of the ecocult's myths, and not a collection of recipes for the future, I seem to have arrived at a totally new and unheard of gimmick: Let the underdeveloped countries decide their own future. Has anyone considered their own wishes? Not Bwana Econut.

How are the underdeveloped countries going to raise the capital needed for the enormous investment of industrialization?

They are already raising it, and by the same means as the White Man raised it: forcible conquest, plunder and robbery. The Spanish plundered the Indians' gold, the French robbed the Spanish, the British pirated it from both; Americans stole an entire continent from the Indian, and almost exterminated him into the bargain; the wealth around us is rooted in the 18-hour a day sweatshops manned by our forefathers in Manchester, Paris, the Ruhr, and Chicago. The underdeveloped countries are not using drastically different methods of plunder. They are nationalizing the White Man's industrial plants, confiscating his property, blackmailing his oil companies, commandeering his ships, annexing vast areas of sea as territorial waters, charging extortionary fees for licenses and permits, and cutting each other's throats in Nigeria, the Congo, the Indian sub-continent, and elsewhere. They have learned the White Man's lessons well.

I do not condone looting and plunder. I am merely observing it.

3

RESOURCES:
Beethoven Depleted Half of
All Classical Music

*In short, we [Americans] are both the looters and polluters
of the globe.*
Paul Ehrlich, *The Population Crisis — Where We Stand.* *

The resources of this planet are finite, the environmentalists keep
telling us; if we don't watch our step, we shall completely deplete
them.

That sounds eminently reasonable. At first sight. But what if we
don't watch our step? Will we then not also deplete the finite
resources of this planet, merely postponing the ultimate catastrophe?
Why is it better to deplete them slowly than rapidly? Is it better to
die over a slow fire than in the electric chair?

The environmentalists have brushed tons of material under the
carpet, but nowhere is their silence more deafening than on this
point, as well it should be: If the resources of this planet are limited,
then catastrophe can be postponed, but not avoided; but if so, why
should we, in Soviet fashion, give up the good life to enable the next
generation to give up the good life to enable . . . the last generation
to be put out of its misery? If doom is inevitable, let's all drink and
be merry, for tomorrow we die; let's deplete, pollute and multiply!

On the other hand, if resources are *not* finite, and something can
be done about it, the econut is in an even worse spot. It is not

* In *Population, Environment and People*, ed. by N. Hinrichs, McGraw-Hill, New
York, 1971.

merely that he is wrong, for he can be proved wrong ten times a day; but you savegely destroy his very *raison d'être*, his most cherished fantasy, the dream of his dreams: doomsday. If doomsday is not coming, he might say with his inexorable logic, then that is the end of the world.

I have searched and searched the ecocult literature for as much as a hint about this point; I have found nothing. With one possible exception. The computer programmers engaged by the Club of Rome must have been faced with this dilemma, for they put the finiteness of resources into the program as one of their assumptions, yet they also wanted to come up with a recommendation on how to save the world. Although they concocted all manner of dependencies to guarantee mankind's suicide (as we shall see in Chapter 5), they could not very well sit on just one horn of the dilemma, and they produced further variants of their suicide machine called "stabilized world models," which are said to require such measures as letting industrial output and capital investment stagnate at their 1975 levels, and which are supposed to ensure mankind's survival. But there are some things not even a computer can take. It will slavishly process data according to the instructions the programmer has provided; it cannot go against them. The instructions say (in effect) that there is 250 years' worth of resources, and that is what the computer works with. In the various variants of this doomsday game, the depletion rate is bent hither and thither, and in two cases resources are even generously doubled, but the computer obediently produces the required doomsday every time, because it has been built in beforehand. In all the apocalyptic variants of this game, naturally, the resources decline in quantity.

But in the "stabilized" variants, which are presented to us as the hope of the world, the computer stubbornly refuses to stabilize as far as resources are concerned; the resource curve goes mercilessly down no matter how the doomsday machine is doctored. And if a million more games were played on this doomsday machine, the resources curve would still go down, for you cannot have it both ways: You cannot assume finite resources first and then hope they will stabilize afterwards. Not even a computer can have his cake and eat it.

What can the newborn discipline of computerized soothsaying do about that? Very simple. The authors of the report limit their "time horizon" even more than their resources. What this amounts to is that they take a pair of scissors and snip off the curves at the year 2100, by which time none of their "stabilized" models have yet

Figure 46 STABILIZED WORLD MODEL I

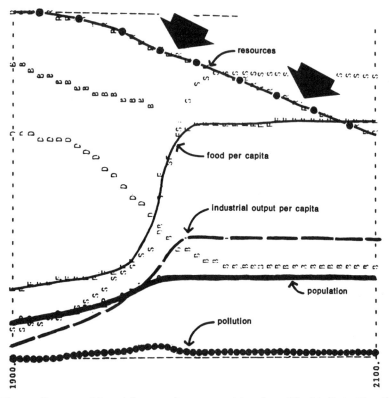

The two figures on this and the opposite page are taken from *The Limits to Growth* (bibliographic reference on p. 10). The arrows, added here and not contained in the original figures, show the curves of declining resources. Their claims to the contrary, the authors have not been able to stabilize their world model; they have merely stopped it at the year 2100.

reached the zero resources that must eventually be reached by this model. The world is, halleluyah, delivered from the threat of catastrophe; not by being advised what to do about resouces, but by a punched card that says STOP. The curves produced by the "stabilized" models are shown in the figures above. It will be seen that the resources curves of these stabilized models have failed to stabilize. They go inexorably down, down, down. All the authors have to say about this is "At the limit, of course, no population or capital level can be maintained forever, but that limit is very far away in time if resources are managed wisely and if there is a sufficiently long time

Figure 47 STABILIZED WORLD MODEL II

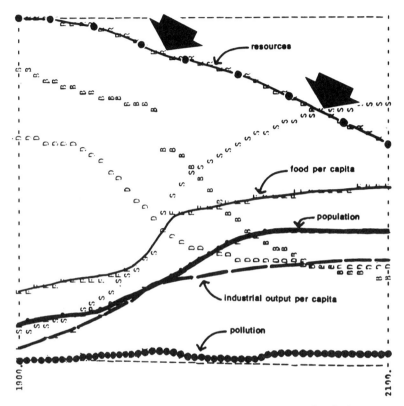

horizon in planning." Please read that statement again; it is a rare instant when someone has sat on the other horn of the dilemma, if only for a fleeting instant (four lines in a whole book). They are saying that if you drink from a bottle more slowly, it will last longer; but how does that prevent the bottle from being emptied? The answer presented by the authors of *The Limits to Growth* is the same as by those who play this game without the benefit of computers: total silence.

They also suggest that people "might choose as a minimum goal that the society left to [their] children can be maintained for the full span of the children's lives." But how exactly do you use finite resources and leave them to future generations as well? The fleeting moment has passed. The authors sit on the first horn of the dilemma again.

What, then, is the answer to the dilemma?

Part of the answer is that we can very easily run out of resources simply by proclaiming them limited; if we do no more than dream up new versions of doomsday machines, we shall certainly deplete them completely. The other part of the answer is that some resources already have been depleted, but scientific research and technological advance have always replaced them by others and have constantly discovered new ones, and that the changing needs of technology have constantly required different raw materials. If scientific research and technological advance is not denied funds, if it is not belittled in the eyes of potential young recruits, if it is not considered less important than the mystic and the occult, then there is not the slightest reason why that longstanding and consistent trend should be reversed.

Non-renewable is not irreplaceable. It is easy to limit resources on punched cards. It is less easy to punch holes into some of the synthetic materials that are now beginning to replace metals, or into the theory that tungsten will not be needed for light bulbs when the light bulb goes from the home into the technical museum. Like other members of the ecocult, the resource fanatics have buried the genuine problems of resource conservation under a mountain of hysteria.

Tнere have been many cases of wanton depletion of natural resources and true crimes against nature. Such crimes were usually not committed by either the use or the abuse of science, but merely by ignorance of it. The poverty of the Balkans, for example, is largely due to the depletion of its forests during three centuries of Turkish occupation; the subsequent soil erosion, dwindling water supplies and the other geological and ecological consequences have turned large stretches of mountainous land in Yugoslavia, Bulgaria and Greece into rocky wastelands.

What is now Israel was once, as the Bible tells us, a "land of milk and honey." It was overgrazed, and most of it is now desert. But what ignorance destroyed, science can bring to bloom again.

Other such crimes against nature have been committed, and are being committed now. The various types of whales in the southern and antarctic seas are now being slaughtered by fishing fleets greedy for shortsighted profit, and the whales, already seriously decimated, are in danger of total extermination. The US government, that pillar of capitalist anarchy, has prohibited all US vessels to hunt whales; but the harpoons of the Soviet government, that pillar of socialist planning, continue the savage slaughter.

In connection with crimes against nature, one hears statements such as these: "The United States has less than 7% of the world's population, but it consumes more than half of its paper. The average American family consumes a ton of paper every year. A single Sunday edition of the New York Times depletes one and a half acres of forests."

Such statements are made by the *imploitation* nut, the world's first nut to have coined a word for himself. The imploitation nut confuses issues. Let us not make the same mistake. One issue is whether the mammoth paper consumption in the United States depletes its forests; a quite different issue is whether it is necessary or wise to use so much paper.

The first issue, whether the timber consumption in the United States depletes its forests is easily answered from the data issued by the US Forest Service, the American Forest Institute, and the US Department of Commerce (no doubt also by other institutions, but the following is based only on these three sources). And the answer is this: The United States is growing about 8% more timber than it consumes. The high crop yield achieved by the forest industry in the United States makes it, in fact, one of the most productive industries in the country. Its high productivity is achieved by scientific and intensive forest management, not by whining about imploitation. And the tree farmers will see to it that it stays that way. If they depleted their forests more rapidly than they could grow them, they would be ruining their own livelihood. That basic truth is not invalidated by wreckers who would cut down the redwoods to make backscratchers; and it is not invalidated by the imploitation nuts who would give Americans guilt complexes for managing their forrests more wisely than, say, the USSR, which has many times more forest land, but is unable to provide its citizens with as much as toilet paper.

The depletion of America's forests by wanton paper consumption is therefore a sham depletion; it is as much depletion as harvesting the land, as much depletion as utilizing a source and managing it so it will never dry up, and as much depletion of classical music as playing a recording of a Beethoven symphony.

The issue here is very simple: It is the difference between unrenewable and unrenewed resources. It is the difference between "a Turkish economy" (an idiom in several languages) that ruined the Balkans, and the American economy that has produced high-yield crops of forest lands.

It is true that not all paper used in the United States comes from timber grown in American forests. But the paper and paper products that were imported were not looted. The United States shelled out one billion dollars for them in 1970. Besides, the imploiters are not worried about foreign exchange; they are worried about American forests which, as we shall see in a moment, need other things than imploitation.

The other issue, whether the timber gained from American forests is used wisely, is almost completely unrelated. Poppy seeds can be used for making pastries, and they can be used for making heroin. What does that have to do with the depletion of the world's poppy seed supply? The use of paper in the United States does not deplete its forests; but whether it is used wisely is a matter of opinion. My own opinion is that its use is wanton and ridiculous. In what other country will they sell you a single picture postcard and put it in a paper bag five times the size of the card? In what other country do you have to search for the product in the package? I remember a cartoon showing a woman meditating over an empty card box; she says "I threw out 6 wrappings, 17 pins, three card boards, two linings, five advertisements, and I must have thrown out the shirt as well."

But the wanton use of paper is not something that need go on forever. Intelligent people buy products, not packaging, and their numbers are increasing. The packaging fad is not an inborn natural desire, quite the contrary. In the *Hidden Persuader*, Vance Packard describes how marketing researchers made a test on what type of packaging appeals most to youngsters. They offered several young-sters to pay for any one product chosen from the shelves of a super-market. They all chose a water melon. It is possible that in this minor problem, at least, the imploitation nuts may have a beneficial effect by doing the right thing for the wrong reason. Similarly, more and more people are discovering that aspirin is aspirin, and all aspirin is FDA approved; if they choose the brand with the big hammer and the ingredient that doctors recommend most (which is aspirin), they are paying for the $60,000 a minute that it cost to advertise it on TV, and for the paper imprinted with similar wisdom. They are paying some kind of tax automatically imposed on the impressionable. Which has nothing whatever to do with the depletion of forests.

But sham depletion is only a small part of the demagoguery practiced by the impoitation nut. Forests have other uses than providing timber. They act as vast water reservoirs, for one thing. If it were not for the forests, Oregon and Washington, for example, would be flooded in March and parched in July. So great is this effect that forests, by evaporation and other mechanisms, affect the climate of entire regions; they act as air conditioners. Perhaps even more important, they are more effective for photosynthesis than any other form of vegetation. Photosynthesis is the process in which water and carbon dioxide are synthesized into carbohydrates (sugar) with the light of the sun supplying the necessary energy, and chlorophyll, the stuff that makes plants green, acting as a catalyst. Oxygen is produced in this chemical reaction. Photosynthesis turns inorganic into organic matter, and together with the production of oxygen, it is therefore the basic life-sustaining process on earth. It is, for example, the basis of all food chains. Jonathan Swift's "fleas that have smaller fleas to bite'em, and so on *ad infinitum*," were feeding on an ox; this ox must have been feeding on grass, and the nutrients of grass are produced by photosynthesis.

But grass and croplands comprise only about one sixth of the world's organic material; only one third of the organic material is in the oceans, although they cover the majority of the globe. The big reservoir of organic materials (nearly one half) are the world's forests. More important, fully one half of all photosynthesis takes place in the forests.

The other process that makes forests particularly important is transpiration. This is the process in which plants ooze moisture into the air, not only humidifying it, but also cooling it by using up the water's latent heat of evaporation. Nature's most important mechanism for cooling and humidifying the atmosphere is evaporation from the oceans; but this is only so because the majority of the globe's surface is covered by water. Acre for acre, the humidifying and cooling activity of a forest is roughly the same as that of the sea. Surely, then, forests are among the most basic of nature's life sustaining engineering feats.

Who would threaten these most basic life-sustaining activities of America's forests? You guessed it: The imploitation nut. Stop interfering with nature, he says, do not upset its delicate checks and balances, do not deplete the forests, start de-developing. What would happen if we followed his advice?

What I have said about America's forests looks like water onto the econut's mill. Half the story is always what keeps the econut's mill in business. The other half is what grinds it to a halt.

Forests are the most efficient of nature's photosynthesis factories, but that efficiency can be far increased by man's aid. There is nothing blasphemous in that statement: A cow or a hen is an animal produced by nature, but very much with man's help — nature alone does not produce birds laying an egg a day, let alone without mating. Nature alone produces deer, but not cows. Nature alone produces grass, but not wheat. Nature alone produces streams to run water wheels, but not dams to run turbines. And nature alone produces virgin forests whose life-sustaining activities are far smaller than those that man can induce in managed forests.

An old forest, left to nature alone, is filled with overmatured trees, and it consumes as much oxygen as it produces. It slows, or even stunts, the growth of younger trees, which are the real operators of both photosynthesis and transpiration. Of course, nature will not let a forest consuming as much oxygen as it produces stand forever. It will weed out the offenders. It attacks them by disease, to which the old trees are less resistant than the young and vigorous ones. It hits the forest with lightning, and the old, dry trees will burn, whilst the few young trees that survive a forest fire will eventually result in a rejuvenated forest growing out of the ashes of the old one. But natural selection and survival of the fittest is no more than a crude and random affair with the odds stacked against stagnation and extinction. Man can do better in rejuvenating a forest than to set it on fire. He can cut the trees before they reach full maturity; he can fertilize the forest so it will grow more quickly; he can spray the trees to protect them against disease; and let me tell you another original thought, Only you can prevent forest fires. Nature is not on Smokey's side.

When man thus manages forests, an acre of forest will consume 5 to 6 tons of carbon dioxide per year. Moreover, it will give off 4 tons of fresh oxygen. If the forest industry did no more than that, they might perhaps become the Robin Hoods of the ecology movement. But in raising the oxygen production from almost nothing to four tons per acre per year, man commits an unforgivable crime in the eyes of the imploitation nut: From that same acre, he also gains four tons of timber. Some of that timber ends up in the garbage published by the imploitation gurus, but that does not make the crime less heinous.

They therefore devise all kinds of schemes to imploit the forests, to save America's trees, and so on. When the various environmental and ecological organizations panhandle by mail, the paper is usu-

ally imprinted with the boast "Made from 100% recycled paper."
Recycled paper, in America, saves trees which do not need saving. It
is probable that the cost of recycled paper is higher than that of
paper made from new fibers, for the paper has to be separated from
other refuse, and the ink and other coating must be disposed of. The
energy needed for the transportation and processing of paper waste
before it reaches the mill is supplied by burning gasolene in trucks
and coal in power stations, whereas the new fibers are produced
directly by the energy of the sun, and quite often the timber is
transported to the paper mill by floating it down a river. The end
product is inferior paper. The effects of recycling paper can perhaps
best be studied in countries that have been recycling paper for
decades. One such country is the USSR, the biggest forest land
owner in the world, another is Czechoslovakia, which has some of
Europe's most luscious forests. Both countries suffer from a chronic
and acute paper shortage. (Take a look at a scientific book published in the USSR some 20 to 40 years ago. The paper is so
yellowed it is often difficult to read the print.) The paper shortage in
the Soviet Empire makes a long and gloomy story, with which I will
not bore the reader, because the question of recycling paper is not
very important. The losses in recycling paper are probably not very
big and can easily be absorbed.

But this is not so with other losses that the imploitation nuts are
beginning to inflict on America's forests. An 8% reserve by which the
growth exceeds the harvest is not very much for a growing demand
for timber. Only 13% of the total commercial forest lands are intensively grown and harvested. Another 22% of commercial forest lands
belong to the federal government and are cared for by the US Forest
Service, a pauper among government agencies. It was the US Forest
Service which pioneered the research and devlopment that resulted
in the high yield timber crops in America, but only 39% of the funds
requested by the US Forest Service over the last 10 years for timber
growing have been approved by Congress. According to the American Forest Institute, 5 million acres of federally owned land lie idle
and in need of restocking, and 13 million more acres, including land
devastated by forest fires and disease, are in need of improvement.

Is the upkeep of America's greatest air purifiers not more important than printing appeals to curb the growth of science and technology on recycled paper? Not to the econuts. They have brainwashed
people into believing that all production is bad, and timber production even worse, because it depletes forests. And naturally, funds are

alloted to where the votes are. Wilderness area, yes (I am all for them); but timber production, no. It would ruin the forests and hurt the ecology. Once again, the econut has come full circle. The imploitation nut opposes keeping America's greatest air purifiers in shape.

For the reasons given above, intensive and efficient management of forests is particularly important. Among the other "renewable" resources, the most important is obviously food. Remember the constant predictions of imminent world famine issued by the Food and Agriculture Organization of the United Nations in the late forties and the fifties? Not much has changed, except the date, when one compares them to Paul Ehrlich's predictions of imminent world famine. But the predicted general world famines have failed to materialize. Most of the world still goes hungry; but food production is keeping abreast of population increase, and the threat of world-wide famine is receding. Perhaps a new edition of the Paddock brothers' book *Famine —1975!* will be published; perhaps it will be called *Famine — 1985!*, and the next one *Famine — 1995!* The reason why these worldwide catastrophies have so far not materialized is that the Jeremiahs, from Malthus onwards, have consistently underestimated what science can do in food production. There is hunger in the world, yes; more than most people realize. But there is less than there was one hundred, or two hundred or five hundred years ago. Food production has, by and large, kept pace with population increase. The last time famine was staved off dramatically was the Green Revolution, another scientific achievement which produced high-yield varieties of grain. In fact, the Green Revolution appears to have created a reserve in keeping food production in the underdeveloped countries well ahead of population growth. There are further reserves not only in arable land to be made fertile by irrigation, but above all in the per-acre yields, which are lamentably low in the underdeveloped countries, and which can do a lot of catching up before a limit is reached. "Farming of the sea" is a further possibility, though the hopes in this field may be strongly exaggerated. Further Green Revolutions may or may not take place; they will certainly not take place if science and technology is de-developed and faults of the past Green Revolution are searched for inch by inch with a magnifying glass until they are located. The Ehrlichs, for example, make the following devastating arguments against the species of cereals introduces by the Green Revolution: "Pesticides and mechanized planting and harvesting are necessary to get the most out of the new varieties. These too are expensive, and capital is in short supply in most underdeveloped countries . . . As attempts are made to spread the Green Revolution to smaller farmers, the need for credit becomes acute . . . We suspect that in the next few years escalating pest problems will cut heavily into 'miracle yields' . . ." And if they don't, one might add, let's see to it that they do, by outlawing DDT and all pesticides. But what's the use? The Ehrlichs have the final answer: "Clearly, one of the prices that is paid for higher yield is a higher risk of widespread catastrophe."

Now whilst it seems to me that at least a temporary respite has been gained by the Green Revolution and other scientific advances, and that the Ehrlichs' attitude is not merely pessimism, but pathetic petulance, I am not saying that this can go on forever. Science has its well defined limits, and it cannot break its own laws. What I am saying is that the *need* for more food production will eventually cease. As the underdeveloped countries become industrialized, their population growth will decline and eventually cease. The population will stabilize as it is stabilizing now in the United States and in Europe. It will be stopped by the same forces that are stopping it in the industrialized countries. Not by collapse and catastrophe, much less by the puerile proposals of coercive legislation, but by the social, economic, perhaps even psychological, circumstances in which people find themselves in an advanced society. In the industrialized countries, people yearn for 15 children no more than they yearn for a sword and shield.

As pointed out earlier, population is a system with a very long time constant. There may be overshoots and oscillations before the system stabilizes in an equilibrium, and this may lead to temporary crises in food supplies just as in other fields. But if the industrially most advanced country is any guide to the future (which it may not be), the overshoot appears to be in the other direction: Food production has far outstripped population growth, and at a time when stabilization of the population is in clear sight, there is enough surplus to supply food to underdeveloped countries, where the economy is backward, and to the Soviet Empire, where the economy is mismanaged. There is admittedly not enough to eliminate hunger altogether; but there is more than enough to make the point that food production in the industrialized countries has far outstripped population growth. In the industrialized countries, nobody *need* go hungry; if some people do go hungry nevertheless, then this testifies to mismanaged social problems, not to insufficient food production. The growth of food production in the industrialized countries is no less than mind-boggling. For example, in the United States, productivity in agriculture has increased by more than 40% since World War II. To see how fantastically high that figure is, one must realize that the basic process has remained unchanged for 10,000 years: The increase in productivity was not achieved by a basic breakthrough in the production of food, but only in the ways in which we guide and push and doctor and manipulate Nature. The basic secret is still unknown to us, for we still do not know what every cow knows: how to turn grass into milk.

Whilst my main point is that we will not run out of food because food production will eventually outstrip the growth of a stabilizing population, there are some secondary points to be considered.

The first is the misconception that the staple foods of man have not changed over the centuries. This is perhaps true of wheat and some other cereals, and of "meat" if understood as the flesh of whatever animal. But it is not true of such staple foods as sugar and the potato, and of such basic forage plants as corn (maize). For many centuries, the only concentrated sweetness that man knew was honey and such juices as maple syrup. Cane sugar reached the West only in the Renaissance, and beet sugar is less than two centuries old. Its discovery, like so many other discoveries, was mothered by necessity. When the British blockaded the Continent during the Napoleonic wars, they cut off the sugar supply from the West Indies. Forced to look for a substitute, Europe found one: In 1799, Franz Carl Achard developed the sugar beet from the white Silesian beet and from wild beets found in Sicily and along the shores of the Mediterranean. The substitute proved to be as good or better than the original: Europe now gets practically all of its sugar from the beet.

The potato was brought to Europe from the New World, and for two centuries it was cultivated as a garden plant for its beautiful flowers; it was thought inedible, for its fruit is poisonous. Apparently it took 200 years for someone to try the root instead of the fruit. Thereafter, the potato became the staple food of generations.

My point in recalling all this is that man is a resourceful animal, in food production as everywhere else, and that the food of tomorrow may be as unknown today as the sugar beet was 200 years ago. The chances are that the reader of this book has some ice cream in the refrigerator. One hundred years ago there was no ice cream. There were not even any refrigerators. How did Chicago get California or Florida oranges in the summer before there were refrigerated railroad trucks? It didn't.

Of course, man can live without ice cream or oranges, but he has proved resourceful in providing more important foods such as beet sugar or the multiple-ear wheat of the Green Revolution.

Salt, like water, is inorganic, and therefore not truly a foodstuff, but man cannot survive without its intake for long. In the Middle Ages Central Europe was, metaphorically speaking, far from the sea and salt was mined. At times reserves dwindled, and salt became so precious that it was used as cash money alternatively (but not equivalently) to gold. The two dimes we pay for a box of salt today probably mostly cover the container, the advertising and the overhead expenses.

I know next to nothing about Franz Carl Achard, the man who developed the sugar beet. But this much is certain about him: He did not whine about doomsday.

My last thought concerning food supplies of the future may sound ridiculous, and it is, indeed, somewhat reckless. All predictors, whether optimistic or pessimistic, skate on thin ice. Yet I believe the thin ice on which I am about to embark is somewhat thicker than that supporting the apocalyptic fantasies: I question the eternal validity of the assumption that only a cow can make milk, and that it can only be made from grass. No, I have not found a better method; but that is no proof that no better method will ever exist. What natural law is there to say that milk cannot ever be synthesized as well and better than natural milk? Does milk contain more than the 92 elements of the Mendeleyev table? Is not a cow the living proof that synthesis of milk is possible?

Until 1828, scientists believed that organic matter could not be synthesized from inorganic matter. Then Friedrich Wöhler produced urea, a substance found in urine, from the ammonium salt of cyanic acid and dumbfounded the scientific world. The world has been dumbfounded by scientific discoveries many times since then. Why should that trend change? Science cannot break natural laws; but there are whole worlds contained between their limits.

The example is symbolic; what I have in mind is synthetic food in general. If you say that this is a pretty (or ugly) fantasy which is totally useless for the problems of next week, you are, of course, quite right. My point is simply that inevitable doom is nothing but a fantasy, and that if you must fantasize, you might as well skate on the thicker parts of the admittedly very thin ice. The Russians have a proverb: The anus is not the most pleasant part of the body. Why can you doomsdaymongers never look anywhere else?

THE eventual depletion of "non-renewable" resources such as mineral wealth is one of the most cherished shibboleths of the doomsday prophets. Without this shibboleth, for example, the Club of Rome's doomsday machine would fall to pieces, even though it is protected against all sanity by hundreds of loops of multiple overkill.

But the truth of the matter is that the overall supply of mineral resources has always been on the increase. Their constant depletion has always been compensated for by three powerful forces: The discoveries of new supplies, the discoveries of replacing old raw materials by different raw materials, and the change in demand for raw materials no longer required as technology advanced and changed its needs.

Not so long ago, in the gold rushes to California and Colorado, the golddigger searched for gold like this: He spun around until he had lost all sense of direction and then threw his hat up and forward into the air; wherever it landed marked the spot where he started digging in the hope of striking it rich.

Is that the method by which we prospect for new resources today? For every inch of depletion, we have advanced a mile in knowledge. We know more about geology and geophysics, and therefore more about where new resources are likely to be hidden. We know more about probability theory, which has proved very fertile in geophysical prospecting. We know more about optimization methods, and we calculate the maximum probability of a strike for a minimum number of drills. We no longer throw hats before we dig or drill; we use the radioactive signals that betray the position of a find. We look for distortions of electric and magnetic fields. We send down sonic and electromagnetic waves and watch how they are bounced back. We set off explosive charges and monitor the propagation of seismic waves through the bowels of the earth to spy on their secrets. We are no longer limited to prospecting on the continents; we are exploring the bottom of the sea as well. As I am writing this, the first satellite to prospect for new resources over the entire globe is being readied (it will also monitor worldwide pollution). These are some of the methods of today. Tomorrow's methods will not be worse, but better.

But this is not all the imploitation nuts have embezzled. With the heart-rending anxiety of the man who is about to overdraw his checking account, they keep on driveling about the thin and delicate layer of the biosphere which is fighting an uneven battle against man's vicious urge for destruction. How much food and fresh air does a layer of iron ore need for survival? It is buried deep down in the bowels of the earth, and we are drilling deeper and deeper. And only delirious de-developers and impertinent imploitation nuts can prevent us from drilling deeper yet.

The depth of the earth is limited, yes. So is the time for which the sun will still shine. But to get an idea of the depth of the earth's outer mantle, take paper and pencil and make this little calculation: What is the depth down to the chord joining two points a mere 100 miles apart on the spherical surface of the earth? Close to 1,000 feet. One thousand feet! We have not even begun to touch what we are walking over.

There are a number of other questions that come to mind even before we turn to the main point that non-renewable is not the same thing as irreplaceable. For example, what is the effect of new technological processes on the rate of depletion of even present supplies? Is it not possible that the depletion of some mineral resources may decline, not due to environmental concerns, but because they are no longer needed? This is not only possible, but highly probable. As we shall see in a moment, the telephone lines of the future are likely to be made not of metal, but of glass. But there are many other such cases where changing technology requires changing materials. For example, steel bridges are now usually welded or bolted. Welding uses up non-ferrous ingredients, and bolts use up steel (and some non-ferrous ingredients, too). But in recent experiments, bridges were glued together with adhesives. Not, of course, because of doomsday stories, but because it may be cheaper, simpler, and it may make the bridge more flexible under mechanical and thermal loads. (This is, as yet, only in the experimental stage.) The advance in the field of adhesives in the last few decades is stunning. There are now glues available that will harden in about one minute to a tensile strength of 100 pounds. Should glueing of bridges prove feasible, safe and profitable, much metal, including non-ferrous metals, will be saved. Not because of imploitation hysterics, but because of technological advances.

The bulk of the bridge is, of course, still made of steel, but steel is not a material that will stay forever. In many applications it is being replaced by synthetic materials, and steel production is no longer much of an economic indicator, as it was in the 19th century. Only the imploitation nuts remain fascinated by the steel production statistics, and they use them in their inscrutable mental acrobatics which appear to rest on the assumption that every ton of steel produced in the United States is a ton of steel stolen from India, which may be their interpretation of Commoner's Law that everything is connected with everything else.

Another example: The word *plumber* comes from the Latin *plumbum*, which means lead, for that was what plumbing used to be made of. In old houses, one may still find real plumbing instead of coppering. What brought about the change? Obviously, the superior properties of copper as compared with lead, which, on balance, made copper preferable for the tubes of a plumbing system; not the imploitation nuts who wanted to conserve lead, for they were not yet around at that time — at least not in their present form, though there have always been people predicting the bottom of the barrel. Now that the price of copper is increasing, synthetic materials are beginning to appear for some pipes carrying water.

But the important point is this: Does non-renewable mean irreplaceable? Take the example of copper, whose alloys are used by the megaton in the electrical industry, mainly because the electrical conductivity of copper is exceeded only by that of silver and platinum, and by not very much at that. In addition, copper is malleable, its alloys have tensile strength as well, and they do not rust or corrode; it is therefore used for the conductors of the millions of miles of transmission lines that act as the arteries of any modern civilization by supplying electric power, and for the telephone lines that act as its nerves. It is also used in transformers, motors, generators, switches, and all other kinds of electrical and electronic equipment from cyclotrons to electrical backscratchers. What, then, will we do if and when we run out of copper? In fact with the presently known supplies of copper in the United States being depleted, and the copper mines in the developing countries being expropriated, the situation is not rosy, though it is not as critical as the imploitation alarmists would suggest. What will we do? Some people know only one solution: Sit down and write essays beginning with "We are in grave, grave trouble." *

---

* The beginning of *The Population Crisis — Where We Stand*, see footnote p. 64.

There are countries which are not in danger of running out of copper; they have already run out of it. The Soviet Union and its colonies, for example, suffer not only from an acute copper shortage, but from a shortage of all nonferrous metals as well. The bureaucrats of the USSR are an imploitation nut's dream: They sit on the world's richest mineral wealth, but they manage to keep most of it underground. Chromium, for example, is bought from Rhodesia by these champions of the oppressed. They also resold it at a big profit to the United States (which until recently did not trade with Rhodesia in keeping with a UN resolution) along with shouts of "You racists!"

Is the Soviet Empire without power lines or telephones? Of course not. But they do not use copper for them, they use aluminum and its alloys. The conductivity of commercial aluminum is about 40% lower than that of annealed or drawn copper; as for the other properties, some are worse (wires bend less easily), some are better (weight). So what? Power transmission is less efficient and more heat is generated in aluminum conductors. But aluminum has proven a satisfactory and workable substitute for copper in much electrical equipment. For telephone lines, energetic efficiency is of secondary importance, and here the lack of copper matters even less; not to speak of the fact that the Soviet telephone network is so atrociously bad that the conductivity of its wires matters as little as if a leper is near-sighted. However that may be, as far as running out of copper is concerned, the imploitation nuts have been put to shame by the managers of the world's most mismanaged economy.

The electrical conductors made of aluminum have not resulted in catastrophe of any kind. Their conductivity is worse than that of copper conductors, but as in all other cases, all factors, and not just one, must be weighed in making a decision. If conductivity were all that mattered, copper would not be used for conductors, either; platinum and silver have higher conductivities.

As a matter of fact, the early investigators of electricity one and a half centuries ago did use a precious metal when they needed a good conductor that could be rolled into very thin sheets; they used a measuring instrument called the gold leaf electroscope, but it can now only be found in technical museums. Not only would it have been unthinkable to use gold in every electrical measurement instrument, but better and totally different systems were invented. We are witnessing something similar right now: The most satisfactory method of eliminating hydrocarbons from the exhaust gases of a car is, to date, a chemical reaction involving platinum as a catalyst. But platinum is about three times more expensive than gold, and anti-pollution devices using platinum border on the ridiculous. But the tough 1975 and 1976 air pollution standards have to be met. Such situations, and the research which they engender, have a habit of coming up with something that is cheaper than platinum and does the job as well or better. Perhaps another catalyst will be found. Perhaps a totally different system of eliminating hydrocarbons will be found. Perhaps, and this is the least probable possibility, society will choose to relax the emissions standards rather than putting platinum in the anti-pollution devices of every car. There are several possibilities; but none of them is catastrophe.

There is another point to be made about aluminum. Until well into the last century, aluminum was a precious metal, and only the very rich had cooking utensils made of aluminum, for then as today, the accepted philosophy was "if it's expensive, it must be good." Then a process was discovered whereby aluminum could be extracted from bauxite, an abundant mineral ore. Today aluminum is so cheap that it is used for a thousand uses, including aluminum foil, which is thrown out after use. An aluminum company now publishes a book-let on how to make Christmas decorations from aluminum foil.

What would people of 150 years ago have said if they had been told that one day aluminum would be so cheap and plentiful that it would be used to make Christmas decorations to be thrown into the garbage a week after Christmas? They knew of no bauxite, just as we do not know of the whatever-ite that will be the raw material of tomorrow. I cannot, of course, prove the second part of that state-ment; however, the burden of proof is not on myself, but on those who ignore the consistent and longstanding trend of the incessant introductions of new processes and utilizations of raw materials that were not utilized before, and whose supply is virtually unlimited. The ores from which aluminum is made, for example, are not in short supply; the McGraw-Hill Encyclopedia of Science and Technology (1965 edition) lists them as "inexhaustible." This may be an over-statement, but I am not worried; if the present supplies of bauxite last only until the year 2,500, or even only until 2,100, I have little doubt that by then new sites of bauxite will have been discovered, or other ores from which aluminum can be extracted will have been found, or most probably of all, aluminum will no longer be needed, because some synthetic material whose properties are superior to those of aluminum will have been developed.

Steel may be a material that is going along that road. Though ultimately always produced from iron ores, the processes of making iron and steel have changed from puddling to production by the open hearth process to producing Bessemer steel to producing electro-steel. But steel is being more and more replaced by synthetic and other materials, and though contemporary technology and consumer goods would still be unthinkable without iron and steel, steel is no longer king, and steel production figures are no longer considered the all-embracing indicator of a country's economic standing (except by Paul Ehrlich, who measures the environmental impact of the birth of a baby by the steel production associated with its nationality). A typical case where steel is being replaced by plastics is demonstrated by (some) gear wheels; they mesh better, last longer, are noiseless, do not require lubrication, and are cheaper.

There is, however, an essential difference between the replacement of steel gears by plastics, and the replacement of copper conductors by aluminum; in the former case the replacement came about by the superior properties of the new material, in the latter it came about by default, for lack of a better material.

The latter case is, I believe, not typical, because its ultimate cause is usually an unforeseen upheaval (such as war) or mismanagement. It appears to be rare to hit onto a better product merely by default. Yet there are such cases: The sugar beet, for one, as we have seen. Another such case is inserted here parenthetically; it has little to do with the point under discussion except that it may (or may have been) a better product by default. Russian technology was very backward before and during World War II, and Russian military radio equipment made Western engineers wince. Typically, a Russian army radio transmitter weighed five or more times as much as its American equivalent; the keying relay drew ten times as much current, which was not surprising, because where Western relays had silver-plated contacts, the Russian relay used two hexagonal nuts of the type to be found on any bicycle. But for once, I am not laughing at the Russians. These were, after all, military transmitters, and where a US transmitter might be quite often in repair, the Russian monstrosity could probably not be put out of action by anything short of a direct hit, and even then, presumably, it could be put together again at the village blacksmith's or at the nearest bicycle shop. As the Russians improved their technology, they followed the American philosophy of "operation by a moron, repair by a genius." I am wondering, in this little parenthesis on better products by default, whether this is the best philosophy for military equipment, and whether a little less sophistication would not sometimes accomplish more. End of parenthesis.

The great advance of the last decades, as far as materials are concerned, is that made in the field of synthetic materials. These need mineral resources only marginally, and they have a number of properties that are unattained by any metal or other substance extracted from mineral ores. There is, for example, no metal that attains the strength to weight ratio of nylon. (The alleged indestructibility of plastics in waste disposal is another hoax of the ecocult.) Apart from their various well known advantageous properties, synthetic materials have another outstanding advantage: The latitude of their properties. The properties of metals are basically fixed; we are more or less stuck with them. Their properties can be manipulated by alloying different metals, but to produce metals with something like optimum properties constitutes an entire science, metalurgy. Like any other science, it has made giant strides in discovering new alloys and new methods of processing to attain certain properties in metals. But metalurgy can do only so much; it can vary various properties such as specific weight, magnetism, malleability, conductivity, melting point, etc., only within reasonable limits, and it cannot overcome certain prohibitions in contradictory requirements; it can often increase one desired property only at the expense of another. The same is true of other "natural" materials, for example, paper. One cannot simply dream up paper with pre-specified properties and ask a paper mill to produce it. As a rule of thumb, one can specify only two of the following three properties: weight, bulk and surface finish. If we want lightweight paper with high bulk (i.e., thick paper, bulking relatively few pages to the inch), we cannot give it a very smooth finish, because "sizing" it will compress it into thin sheets. The requirements are contradictory.

Synthetic materials have, generally speaking (though you could easily prove me wrong in specific cases), much wider latitudes in this respect, and they promise wider latitudes still in the future. In many cases, plastics can already be manufactured "à la carte," that is, from the specified requirements, the chemist can often work out the chemical structure needed to result in the required properties, and then go into the laboratory and produce the material. I am not, of course, saying that you can walk into a chemical lab and ask a chemist to synthesize a material with all the properties of a hamburger; you cannot even ask him to produce a material which is both magnetic and elastic. Nevertheless, one can ask a chemist to synthe-size materials with much "wilder" properties than could be asked of a metalurgist in alloying metals. Moreover, synthetic materials and plastics, being a much younger science, are now advancing at a more rapid pace than metalurgy.

Synthetic rubber, one of the earliest successes of producing a "natural" material synthetically, is a case where man has learned to do without a natural resource; though we still need a cow to make milk, we no longer need a rubber tree to make rubber. Like the sugar beet, synthetic rubber was a child of necessity; it was feverishly worked on in both America and Germany during World War II, when both countries wer cut off from the rubber plantations of the Far East.

The semiconductor industry, to simplify things a little for the sake of briefness, is essentially a crystal growing industry. The germanium crystals (and many others) that grow in nature for epochs, and some that are not grown by nature at all, are grown in laboratories and industrial plants in a matter of days and hours. Crystal growing, too, is a child of necessity. It started not with semiconductors, but with quartz crystals which, when properly cut, will resonate at their natu-ral mechanical frequency determined by the thickness of the slice cut out of the crystal, and at the same time produce a small electrical voltage oscillating at this stable frequency (or its multiple). Before the war, frequency stabilization by quartz crystals was used only in precision electronic equipment and by radio transmitters. They used quartz crystals grown for geological ages by nature. Then, during the war, it became necessary to stabilize the radio frequencies of trans-mitters in thousands of aircraft, tanks, ships and trucks, for it is not at all an easy matter to keep a radio circuit of, say, a squadron of aircraft tuned to the same radio frequency so they can talk to each other and to their base. The allies discovered a way of cutting and mass producing the necessary quartz crystals, and so highly did they value this discovery that they equiped the crystals in aircraft with special detonators that were activated by the impact of a crash and exploded the crystal, so that the Germans would not discover the way in which it was cut, even if the rest of the electronic gear, such as advanced navigational radar, fell into their hands. The principle of the quartz crystal for frequency stabilization is now obsolete, for masers can stabilize frequencies with an accuracy that is some one hundred thousand times better. The quartz crystal principle is now being offered as the latest break-through by a watch company. The model before that, which "goes hm-hm" was based on the principle of stabilizing a frequency by a tuning fork, a child of the 1920's. What is, however, new about these watches is the way in which electronic circuits can now be miniaturized. "Integrated Circuits" are electronic circuits contained in flat sheets that are now being sold by the yard at a price which is negligible compared to what the price of a single component of a circuit used to be 15 years ago. The "chips" in computers are complicated circuits contained in little rectangles roughly the size of a fingernail. The early computers used in the forties had as much as 24,000 thousand vaccum tubes, all unreliable and generating large quantities of heat. They occupied entire buildings. Equivalent contemporary computers are the size of a washing machine. Had the doomsday prophets been around in the forties, and had they correctly predicted the number of computers and their capacities of today, they would have had to conclude that mankind was doomed through lack of space taken up by all those computers. Their predictions would have come to grief, not by inaccurate predictions of the number of computers, but by their stock phrase "if present trends continue."

Synthetic materials cannot, of course, replace *all* mineral resources, at least not directly. Such metals as molybdenum or tungsten are chemical elements and therefore, by definition, they can neither be broken up or chemically synthesized. But here again, this is not doomsday knocking at the door. The idea of making elements by transmutation is, at present, as far fetched as making milk without cows, though the possibility is proven. However, to produce the amount of tungsten needed to make a few light bulbs by transmutation in a nuclear accelerator would, at present, be akin to emptying the Great Salt Lake with a tea spoon. The principle, of course, is feasible, and some day someone may invent the equivalent of a mammoth tea spoon to do the job. But we do not have to resort to such flimsy hopes to see that here, too, the imploiters' arguments are fallacious. These elements are not sacred cows in whatever application they are used; they are used for certain of their properties, and there is no reason why these properties could not be produced in a material or chemical that is *not* an element. Moreover, demand changes not only for materials, but also for their properties. Demands for properties change; they have always changed, they are changing, and there is no reason to suppose that they will not continue to change. In all probability, therefore, we are talking about a non-problem: We may be thinking of materials whose properties will not be required when the time comes. As a typical example, take the tungsten (or osmium or wolfram or whatever other element) used for the filaments of light bulbs. These elements have little to do with the generation of light as such; they are put in there because they have a very high melting point and make the bulb last longer. Thomas Alva Edison did not need any of them for generating light by a light bulb; but his first bulbs lasted only for a day or two. What would be needed to replace these elements is simpy another material to withstand high temperatures with the right order of electrical resistivity. Where is it written that such a material must be an element?

Yet this is still only scratching the surface of the issue. The more important point is that in the year two thousand something, nobody will want to touch light bulbs with a five-foot sterilized pole, and nobody will therefore be looking for a material with such properties. For the light bulb is already an outdated contraption that belongs into technical museums. Its efficiency is about 5% and often less; only rarely does it reach 10%. That means that only about 5% of the watts it consumes are turned into light; the rest is wasted as heat. This is roughly the efficiency of James Watt's steam engine of some two centuries ago. It is hard to find another energy convertor in 1972 with such an apallingly low efficiency. And there is no reason other than ingrained tradition to use it for illumination of rooms any more. A (fluorescent) strip light has an efficiency of better than 40%, and its color spectrum is much closer to the spectrum of sunlight than that radiated by a light bulb. It has a much longer life, and according to the best available evidence, it is no harder on one's eyes than a light bulb, and probably less hard, because it does not cast sharp shadows. Strip lights, of course, do not need any tungsten or osmium or anything else with a high melting point. Their light is generated by a totally different principle; the gas in them is ionized by the electric field of the electrodes, resulting in ultraviolet radiation, which is absorbed by the fluorescent coating on the glass, where it is changed into light. The strip light, of course, is not here to stay forever, either, because 40% is better than 5%, but still nothing to write home about. But the trend of the story from the torch to the strip light is clear: we are slowly but surely moving toward the ideal of "cold light," the secret of which is known to the firefly, but not to us — as yet. What resources should we conserve now to make it easier for our children or grandchildren to make cold light? Again we run into all the difficulties of attempting to regulate a system with a long time constant, of turning the steering wheel now for the curve coming in 25 years, or 250 years, in the road that nobody has ever seen. If we de-develop tungsten mining now, we shall have to de-de-develop it later, and perhaps de-de-de-develop it after that. We shall not make it easier on future generations by this de-de-de-development; all we shall do is make the present generation stutter.

The example of tungsten in light bulbs is typical and could be repeated for many other cases. How will we make telephone lines when all the copper is gone and all the aluminum as well? It is highly probable that the telephone lines of the future will not need electrical conductivity at all; they will be made of glass fibers acting as waveguides for laser beams. We already know that one such fiber can carry millions of telephone conversations, though we have not yet mastered the required technology. Much of this research is carried on by the Bell Telephone Laboratories. But Bell is Big Business, and an outcry goes up when Bell, shackled by a myriad of regulating agencies, needs more money to fund this and other research. Not one of the ecohysterical organizations will fail to join the holy crusade against Big Business; the Bell Labs will not get their funds; telephone service will deteriorate; and the rate of depleting copper and aluminum resources will accelerate. The econut starts out with imploiting and ends up with depleting.

In 1957, I attended a conference of radio engineers in Sofia, Bulgaria. The Bulgarian hosts had made special briefcases for the delegates and when they were presented, a Bulgarian official made a little speech apologizing in all seriousness that Bulgarian industry was not yet sufficiently advanced to make plastics, and that therefore for the time being we would have to console ourselves with briefcases made of genuine leather; but that he hoped next time a radio engineers' conference took place in Bulgaria, the delegates would be presented with briefcases made of real plastic. At the time, we thought it touching, embarrassing, and very funny. But looking back on that episode, I can see that the man was a thousand times right. Synthetic material *is* better than leather, in all respects except one: It is too cheap. If it cost $300 a yard, Jacqueline Onassis and Elizabeth Taylor would not be seen in anything else. In all other respects, a material like Corfam is better than leather; it is lighter, more flexible, softer, stronger, more durable, easier to clean, and it is not ruined by heavy and continued exposure to water. Alas, it is made too quickly; it does not take years to graze cattle to produce the hide and further complicated processing to turn it into leather. It is fortunate that the gears in kitchen appliances or phonographs are hidden away to hide their shame, or they would still be made of metal.

One could continue like this with ferrites and a hundred other miracle materials invented in the comparatively recent past. But this is not a book on the marvels and miracles of science; it is a book of rebuttals attempting to dispel the myths disseminated by the environmental fanatics and the apocalyptic apostles. I have no stocks in the synthetic materials industry, I merely wish to show how depletion of natural resources is offset by discoveries of more and different resources, and how the natural trend of advancing technology is away from "natural" materials, and away from presently desired properties of materials. On looking at the evidence in such fields as crystal growing or synthesizing materials, how can one be afraid of doomsday because some resources are in presently known supply only for a few more centuries?

But plastics are indestructible, says the econut. So is his logic. If it is non-renewable, don't use it, use something indestructible instead, for if it is indestructible, don't use it either. Nothing is feasible except the two possibilities he has set his heart on: a return to the caves or doomsday.

Plastics, in any case, are not indestructible. They can be combusted at high temperatures and they can be chemically processed to yield low-pollution fuels for burning in thermal power plants, the same power plants that now pollute by burning coal and other polluting fuels.

In spite of all this, there is no denying that there may be temporary and serious shortages of some materials. Such shortages have already occurred and some more, especially fuel shortages, loom dangerously on the horizon. But in none of these cases is the shortage due to the phony depletion principle; it is usually caused by such things as economic mismanagement, politics and the like, and in the near future, fuel and power shortages may be caused, above all, by the ecocult. A few years ago, there was a silver shortage. Silver is needed for coins, photographically sensitive emulsions, and wherever extremely high electrical conductivity is needed. But the dimes in our pockets are proof that non-renewable is not irreplaceable; looking at them sideways one can see that they are sandwiched. The shortage was not caused by exhaustion of all supplies. There are tons of silver in the Rocky Mountains, for example, but it is no longer profitable to mine it. In any case, the shortage soon passed away, and many speculators who had hoarded silver in the hope that the price would go up got badly stung.

But other shortages cannot be laughed off as easily as the silver shortage that never materialized. Above all, this cannot be done with the approaching energy crisis, which is in part a shortage of fuels, especially oil and natural gas. As usual, this is a sham shortage, because it is not caused by lack of resources. It is caused by lack of access to these resources, and the man preventing that access is, once again, the econut.

The United States now imports close to one half of its oil needs from overseas. Most overseas oil supplies lie in countries well within the grasp of Soviet claws, a grasp that is either within easy reach or already accomplished. If present trends continue (a stock phrase borrowed from the ecocult), the Soviet navy will be able to strangle off the remaining supplies within years, for its ships are already superior to outdated American vessels, and it threatens to become superior in sheer numbers as well. The discovery of large oil deposits in Alaska is, under these circumstances, a godsend. A narrow strip of land through Alaska is all that is needed to support a pipeline from the northern shores of Alaska to the icefree ports of the Pacific. Its construction is well planned, and it can be constructed with negligible impact on the environment. But for years the environmental fanatics have sabotaged the project with every possible use and abuse of legal injunctions and propaganda. At the time of writing, the pipes still lie idly at Alaska's ports, waiting to be installed.

More oil lies in the oil shale deposits under the Rocky mountains and elsewhere. There is even less hope of getting the oil out of them, because ecohysterics have helped to tie up the entire affair into a virtually impregnable boondoggle.

Vast supplies of natural gas lie untapped under the surface of the United States. Not all the blame for failing to access them can be put on the ecocult. The Federal Power Commission has so regulated prices of domestic natural gas (and permitted imports at double the price) that exploration and drillings have dramatically decreased. But this is merely the result of imprudent regulation which, one hopes, can be rectified. On the other hand, the ecohysterical organizations are blocking access to natural gas supplies intentionally, because they are slaves to a false philosophy. One project to access natural gas supplies, called Project Rulison and sponsored by the Atomic Energy Commision, was designed to free supplies lying under the surface in south west Colorado by an underground atomic explosion, and to tap the supplies from the cavity formed by the explosion some six months after it. Never was such a furor seen. Murder, arson, rape, pestilence and doom, screamed the econuts. Death by radioactivity, malformed children for generations, atomic holocaust. Not one bugaboo of the econuts' arsenal of horror tales was left unused, not one organization of the ecocult failed to join the crusade. On the contrary, new organizations were formed with the express purpose to kill Project Rulison. Bumper stickers, presumably made of recycled paper, appeared everywhere; "Colorado — playground of the AEC," said some of them. The AEC, the Federal government, the State of Colorado, and anyone else the econuts could find, were hit with legal suit after suit. Injunctions were flying around like sparks from a blacksmith's anvil. The econuts fought Project Rulison inch by inch with the doggedness of a lioness defending her young. They succeeded in delaying the project, but not in preventing the explosion; after all legal maneuvers were finally exhausted, the explosion went off. Were the econuts swept away in atomic holocaust? Of course not. Of all people, the AEC knows something about radioactivity. The radioactivity of the atmosphere around Rulison and over Colorado did not increase by one milliroentgen. Not one leg of one gnat was broken.

Did that cure the econuts and Neo-Luddites? If they could not prevent the explosion, they could at least keep the gas down there, miles under the earth's surface. And they do. They filed more suits, they got more injunctions, they belch more propaganda on how resources are drying up. The six months expired long ago. The gas is still down there waiting to be tapped.

That pathetic story could be repeated a hundred times over. In 1956, American scientists proposed to girdle the globe with a ring of resonant dipoles by putting small strips of tinfoil into orbit. These strips would reflect microwaves back to earth and enable communication by microwaves around the globe. The project, called West Ford, was published and put to the country and the world for discussion. Few responsible scientists raised any objections. Most objections came from people who knew less about resonant dipoles than a goat knows about the gold standard.

It was one of the earlier cases of screaming murder, arson, rape and pestilence. The atmosphere would not get enough sunlight. Astronauts would run into the dipoles and be shot down like ducks. A chain reaction would be set off that could only end in doom and holocaust. In those days, such drivel was not taken seriously, and in

1960, West Ford went ahead. The diploe belt scattered radio waves as predicted. The experiment succeeded. Five years later, as the scientists had predicted, the dipoles sank to the denser parts of the atmosphere, where they burnt up harmlessly. They are now gone and forgotten. But that was five years later.

When Project West Ford was launched, another uproar of murder, arson, rape and pestilence went up in this country and across the world. I was in Czechoslovakia at the time, and the Czechoslovak Academy of Sciences, pushed by its political watchdogs, appointed a committee of astronomers and radio engineers, of which I was one, to investigate the matter. The hope was to get scientific proof of this latest atrocity of American imperialism. We considered the momentum on collision with a satellite; we considered the diffraction of light rays; we considered the effects on the atmosphere; we considered every other reasonable and unreasonable possibility; we found nothing wrong with the American project. The finding of the committee was unanimous. Needless to say, it was never published.

Where are they now, these warriors against West Ford, the fanatics against Kannikin, the wreckers of Rulison, the Jeremiahs of moon-imported disease, the saboteurs of the SST, and the veterans of another thousand predictions proved wrong a thousand times? They are concocting new horror chains that start with supersonic flight or new methods of power generation or anything else, but inevitably end up with the one and only possible outcome: doomsday. They have hundreds of such chains today, and they will have more tomorrow. Perhaps the galaxies will fly apart because we do not eat the right kind of peanut butter.

But other things will fly apart before the galaxies if we listen to the doomsdaymongers.

If the ecofreaks, imploitation nuts and Neo-Luddites have their way, fuels and power supplies will run out not in the twenty-five seventies, but in the nineteen seventies. If they had their way, they (and everybody else) would first get brown-outs, and then black-outs. They would first feel chilly, and then freeze. They would first ride compacts, then scooters, then bicycles. The New York freeways would at last be rid of traffic jams. Los Angeles would at last be rid of smog. The slogan-loving ecocult would find itself a new motto: All the garbage of our gurus for a gallon of gas.

What then? One might envisage at least one development if such circumstances should arise. With the consistency that is their hallmark, the ecofreaks will rise as one man and call for the bulldozers to get on with the strip mining; for the dynamite charges to ruin the Rockies and break through to the oil shale; for the tractors to run in droves through the Alaskan tundra; for the chain saws to cut down the redwoods; for atomic explosions to free more natural gas; for the archives of environmentalism to be burned in the power stations. Conservation? A concept coined by the eggheads in academia. Depletion? A trick of Big Business to hold on to its wealth. Too much technology? The engineers' fault that there is not enough of it. The Alaskan moose? Uses up oxygen.

An exaggeration? Yes; for it is not very likely that the econuts will have their way after the first phases of an energy crisis arrive in earnest, if they do arrive at all. Nevertheless, this is what the ecocult is pushing for with its opposition to power plants and all other types of technology. Unwittingly, but very effectively, the environmental fanatics, imploitation nuts and Neo-Luddites are working for an orgy of pollution and depletion. Every injunction to delay the construction of a nuclear power station, for example, brings them nearer to that outcome.

SPACE is a resource, too. The question of living space does not arise; long before there is "standing room only," there will be no place to put the garbage. San Francisco is running out of land fills, so is New York. Stop-gap solutions will therefore be found, because they will have to be found, but this cannot go on forever. Suffocating in garbage is therefore another alarm drum in the apocalyptic apostles' arsenal of multiple overkill.

Let me repeat that I do not use the name "econut" for everybody who calls for sanity and a clean environment; I use it only for those who think that a better environment can be gained by curbing science and technology, and that doomsday is the penalty for failing to curb them. The waste disposal problem is merely another example showing that there are no solutions without more and better technology.

Waste and refuse is another byproduct of success. Technology brought the success, and poor planning made the wastes a problem. It is a problem which cannot be solved by undoing the success, but by applying advanced technology to eliminate it.

The garbage explosion in the industrialized countries, and particularly in America, is not due to technology growing less efficient, but to the affluence it has brought about; people use more products, and they throw out more of them. When I was a child, shoes were soled six or seven times before they were thrown out (leather soles wore out much more quickly than the presently used foam rubber) and my mother used to pay me the equivalent of a dime for every pair of socks that I darned myself. Socks were not thrown out in those days just because they had several gaping holes in them. Should we go back to darning socks again? Yes, says the mentality (if not the literal text) of the *Last Whole Earth Catalog*. But most people have more productive uses for the time spent in darning socks, and for most people that time is worth more than the money spent on a new pair of socks; it was technology, of course, which lowered the price of socks and raised the income of most consumers to such an extent that this barter of time against money became worth while. But the result of all this is more socks in the garbage dump; more bottles, cans, refrigerators and cars. Are we therefore doomed to suffocate in our own filth?

Yes, if we turn from technology toward witchcraft. Yes, if we try to go back to the caves (which must have been pretty filthy) instead of forward to nuclear power. The unchecked piling up of refuse is no more essential to an industrialized society than pollution is essential to a power station.

It is all very simple, says the super-simplifier and the reversionist. Reduce population, curb production, de-develop, and what little garbage there will be can be recycled. Once more he wants to cure the patient of high blood pressure by beheading him. But society is no more willing to do without its amenities than a man is willing to have himself beheaded. There are better ways to approach the problem. For example, to look at it first and suggest solutions afterward.

The first thing that any investigator will probably note is that the ominous aspect of garbage is not its mass, but its volume. The second obvious thing is that it is all mixed up, broken bottles with tin cans, and lamp shades with melon peels. It also stinks. In short, garbage is low-density, highly inhomogeneous material with an unpleasant odor. This suggests two answers as to what to do with it: Either put these properties to good use, or change them. There appears to be no good use for unprocessed garbage, so consider the other way. To increase the density of garbage, it must be compressed, and this is one very hopeful method of garbage disposal; to make it homogeneous (physically, not chemically), it must either be homogenized by crushing it into small particles and mixing them, or it must be sorted into groups each of which is reasonably homogeneous, and both of these two additional methods (when automated) are being used with increasing success. This makes three basic methods of physical processing (the odor either disappears of its own or is easily eliminated, for the decaying organic matter is also the one with the lowest density). These can be combined with chemical methods of processing, including burning as a fuel.

There are also some suggestions which are evidently impractical. For example, it has been suggested to shoot garbage into outer space. Such suggestions come from the science fiction buffs, who can at times be quite as funny as the econuts. There is, of course, no danger of pollution; to shoot a few billion tons of garbage into the solar system is incomparably less pollution than a fly relieving itself into the Pacific Ocean. However, the energetic balance would be absurdly inefficient. The energy necessary to accelerate a pound of matter to a velocity that will liberate it from the earth's gravity is so large that it is simply ridiculous to waste it on a pound of garbage. There are a thousand other objections, which need not detain us; a society which begrudges funds spent on launching space probes to Mars, but would be willing to send its coffee grinds there would deserve no better than doomsday.

Much more popular, if not much more realistic, are the various proposals of separating household trash into its various components before it is picked up. This is a method which has been tried very often. It has been tried in war time by appealing to the patriotism of the citizenry, and it has been used for decades, by coercion, in the Soviet Empire. But the process is both inefficient and wasteful, and people are not easily persuaded, much less coerced, into cooperating. Sorting garbage into food refuse, glass, metals, bones, and whatever other components that need to be separated for recycling in households is a manual process; it may seem trivially easy when considered per household, but its inefficiency and wastefulness soon become apparent when it comes to collecting these groups of bits and pieces. The administrative difficulties are just one aspect of the inefficiency of a manual process that could be automated; another aspect is the waste of energy (and, at present, additional pollution) in running one truck to collect bones, another to collect paper, and so on. The other difficulty is that of persuading people to cooperate. They did cooperate, for example, in Britain during World War II. But in a war that the population considers just, people will support all kinds of inefficiency (such as using horses instead of trucks) because they know it to be a temporary necessity; they will not accept it as a way of life. Coercion is even more inefficient: The trash collectors of the occupied countries in Europe during World War II saw to it that the stuff would get mixed up again. In the Soviet Empire, such sabotage is not due to patriotism; it is due to the general boondoggle of the way in which things are run, but the end result is much the same. A coercive system always ends up with more trash-collector watchers and watchers of the trash-collector watchers than trash collectors.

These are not generalities that I personally consider probable. The experimental evidence shows that not even such a simple thing as returnable bottles and deposits will make a majority of people, or even a large minority, cooperate. *Fortune*, which presumably has no more reason to be beholden to its advertisers pushing returnable bottles than to its advertisers pushing disposable cans, summarized the various reports on this item by a large number of such diverse groups as the University of Pennsylvania, a group of beverage and container associations, and the Environmental Protection Agency. The reader is referred to the original article for some illuminating details,* but the upshot of it is that whilst half or more of the people questioned in opinion polls allege they would rather see recyclable bottles, the hard facts show that in practice the vast majority of consumers rejects them. The many studies differ only in whether they consider the system as an unimportant improvement or a definite exacerbation of the problem. To give but one example of the unexpected difficulties met even in such a "simple" problem, it was found that if the deposit is more than doubled (from 2 to 5 cents), this makes little difference to the returns; but if the deposit is raised even higher, it may encourage a counterfeit bottle industry. Such points are rarely consider by those who have a simple solution for every problem: legislate, regulate, prohibit, tax. "Heavy deposits, perhaps 25 cents per beer can or 'pop' bottle, should be required," advocate the Ehrlichs. "Then even those that might be discarded would be gleaned from roadsides and beaches by ambitious small boys."† This overlooks not only counterfeit bottles, but also the fact that beverage containers currently make up only something more than 20% of the littered items along US highways (by count), and the ambitious little boys would be inclined to pass over the other 80%.

---

* T. Alexander, *The Packaging Problem is a Can of Worms*, Fortune, June1972.

† *Population, Resources, Environment*, W.H. Freeman & Co., San Francisco, 1970; p. 129.

But perhaps that can be taken care of, too: "Laws might be passed that would place heavy taxes upon any product or wrapping that is designed to be discarded rather than returned or recycled, and the manufacture of nonbiodegradable products could be prohibited."

This proposal would prohibit aluminum foil, wire staples, bottles, cans, jugs, glasses, manicure files, hair pins, plastic sandwich bags and a thousand other products used in every home; but what is more laughable still is the idea that they could simply be legislated out of existence. One might perhaps pass a law like this: "Whoever manufactures a glass product shall be imprisoned for 5 years. Whoever manufactures a metal product shall be imprisoned for 20 years. Products made of plastics must not be manufactured at all."

Here, as elsewhere, the simplistic solutions of the instant environmentalists are self-defeating. For example, the attacks on plastic packages used for meat and vegetables in supermarkets overlook that this type of packaging enables heavily putrescible wastes such as fish heads, meat trimmings or corn cobs to be left outside the city, thereby alleviating the urban garbage problem. Moreover, for some produce such as lettuce and grapes, spoilage is reduced from 20% to 2%, because the packaging is protective, and this is an additional reduction of the urban garbage problem. With what must by now be systematic monotony, we once again find the instant environmentalist unwittingly, but effectively, on the side of the polluters and waste makers.

Apparently much money has gone into theoretical research on recycling and garbage disposal. But $30,000 granted to a team of researchers of the US Bureau of Mines in 1967 (a very small amount where major experimental research is concerned) turned out to be an unusually good investment. The team investigated the ashes taken from urban garbage incinerators and found them equivalent to pretty high grade metallic ore. Using only regular machinery used in the mineral mining industry, not machinery developed for this problem, they found it fairly easy to separate this incinerator residue into ferrous metals, nonferrous metals, glass, and remaining material by the use of crushers, screens, magnets, and other such equipment. The remainder that had to go to the landfill was substantially reduced in volume. Later, the US Bureau of Mines found that an equally good job could be done with unburned trash. The researchers first separated paper, plastics, and other organic matter from the garbage. The steadily increasing fraction of dry paper and plastic is steadily raising the fuel value of household garbage to the point where it has now reached about half the fuel value of coal. That fuel value is now most often wasted; it disappears through the stacks of urban incinerators and does nothing but pollute the air.

Yet this part of the garbage can do more than act as a mere fuel: It can be processed into a fuel with low sulphur content, i.e., into a fuel with low pollution potential. This can be done by sophisticated methods used in the petroleum industry, by which paper, plastics, food processing wastes and other organic matter can be turned into fuels such as oil, gas and coke. Note that the raw materials for this process include "indestructible" plastics, a prime target for the environmental fanatic. By some estimates, organic wastes in the United States are produced in sufficient quantity to supply about half the fuel needs of the country. I do not know enough chemistry or other sciences involved in such claims, and I cannot judge them; what I do know is that even if the claim is ten times exaggerated, chemical processing of organic trash is still a better way to go than to whine about doom by suffocation in garbage.

And this is only the organic part separated from the garbage. Among the remainder is glass, including the bottles that nobody wants to return. Glass can be crushed into a fine material called "cullet" in the glass industry. In bygone days, when manual labor was cheaper and less easily replaced by automation, it was considered worth while to sort bottles of different colors by hand before crushing them and the cullet was used for speeding the processes of glass manufacture. Then its use declined. But today, when optical scanners are taking over the job of card punches because they can read typewritten material (though simple scanners still need special fonts), it is an easy matter to distinguish objects and particles by color. The canning industry, for example, uses optical filters and photocells to detect color differences (and hence different grades) of peas and beans. The electrical signal generated in the photocell for a particular color is amplified and activates air jets to divert a falling stream of objects into different bins. The experimenters of the US Bureau of Mines used no more than a modified pea sorter of this kind to separate the grains of the cullet by color, and were eminently successful.

Would it not have been a better investment to have given the research team at the US Bureau of Mines $3 million, or even $30 million, instead of a beggarly $30,000 for such vital research? $30 million is a lousy 15 cents per inhabitant of the U.S.A., each of whom threw out an average of 464 pounds of paper, paperboard, glass, metals, woods, and plastics (not counting other solid wastes) in 1966, and who is throwing out much more now. But if the experimenters of the US Bureau of Mines did not get $30 million in 1967, they are less likely to get them now. One of the things that has changed since then is the increased technophobia, which has inevitably led to further cuts in research budgets.

Cullet can also be used for many other applications, such as "glassphalt" to pave roads. This has been used experimentally for a number of years in Europe and has been found to have good properties in this application. One of its fringe benefits is that owing to a physical phenomenon known as dispersion, the glass in the paving makes the color of the road change for different angles of incidence of the sun's rays. In a road that leads straight ahead, the hills and valleys of the road can therefore be seen by a driver due to the change in color long before he reaches them, which is not the case now (except for very steep hills and deep valleys).

Whilst many cities are in danger of running out of land fills, Franklin, Ohio, had already all but reached that point in 1967. The city council, therefore, would have had more reason to get the doomsday dithers than the various theorists who write dissertations on apocalyptic holocaustology. But the city council also included Mr. Joe Baxter, a sixty-four year old engineer, who designed a machine on the principle of a hydrapulper (a sort of giant kitchen blender used in the paper industry) which was filled with several truckloads of garbage and with water. The rotating blade of the pulper crushes glass into cullet, shreds plastics, wads cans into fist-sized balls (the water washes and delabels them), and the food and paper wastes are pulped into a thin soup. From here it is a comparatively simple matter to separate the various raw materials by their differences in dimensions and other properties for further processing. About a third of the residues of the process are plastics and other organic matter. This is now burned in an incinerator, but in principle it could also be used as a fuel, for example, for power generation. What Mr. Baxter started became the most advanced, automated recycling plant in the country. It now has a capacity of 150 tons a day, of which only 50 tons are needed to handle the daily refuse of the city.

How oppressive are the taxes that must be imposed on the citizens to support such a plant? This is how oppressive: The plant produces paper pulp that sells at $25 a ton and iron scrap that sells for $15 a ton. Further oppression will set in in November 1972, when the plant will begin to produce color-sorted cullet worth up to $20 a ton and aluminum worth $150 a ton. It looks like Franklin, Ohio, will not pass city ordinances compelling its citizens to sort refuse and to buy returnable bottles. But then, Mr. Baxter did not understand that there is too much technology around us already without his silly gadgets. What he should have done was simply to say "We are in grave, grave trouble."

Only a few years ago, a garbage compactor for household use became available. It compresses the household garbage that would fill a 20 gallon trash can into a small, hard prism. It runs on household current, crushes bottles and cans, and when the container is filled, the "brick" is pulled out in the plastic bag that lined the container. The required electric power and the pollution presently accompanying its generation is utterly negligible compared with the energy consumption and pollution by the trucks hauling the additional volume of uncompressed garbage. (The low efficiency of the internal combustion engine makes the fuel consumption of a truck only partly dependent on the payload.) It may well be that the garbage compactor will become a household appliance as widespread as the refrigerator or the washer. Yet this is only a very modest example of compression. Need I go on to fantasize about the pressures attainable in the future, about the pressures and mass densities attained on distant stars, about the fact that all matter is mostly empty space, and that the molecules contained in the contents of a 20 gallon trash can could ultimately be compressed into a space no larger than the dot of the question mark ending this sentence? I think not; perhaps I have made the point without fantasies by pointing to examples of what is experimentally proven here and now.

Let me summarize this point as follows: If you want to suffocate in refuse later, start de-developing now.

ALL of the above was concerned with household refuse. Industrial wastes that pollute rivers and other industrial wastes that pollute the air are inseparably bound up with problems of energy conversion, and they are bound up with them in precisely the opposite way of what the apostles of apocalypse would have us believe: Curbing pollution demands more electric power, not less. In the next chapter, we will go on to this fundamental question that the ecocult has managed to confuse and obscure with fanatical fervor. But in connection with the simplistic approach to waste disposal proposed by many instant environmentalists, one cannot help noting that all to often we are prisoners of simple popular wisdoms that may be pretty good advice for general tendencies, but which are patently false in particular cases. "Prevention is better than cure" is such a popular wisdom; "Waste not, want not" is another.

"Prevention is better than cure" is something that is not universally valid. Maintenance policies for replacing components of a complex system can today be precisely calculated by the mathematical methods of reliability theory. In repair maintenance, components are replaced on failure; in preventive maintenance they are replaced at a certain age (or on failure if they fail before they have reached that age). In many cases, for which the exact criteria are now well known, it turns out that prevention is *not* better than cure; preventive maintenance in those cases will result in more wasted components, longer down times and higher costs than repair maintenance. The popular wisdom is then an erroneous generalization.

"Waste not, want not" can also lead one astray if it is understood as an inflexible dogma. It has led many environmentalists astray because they base their conclusions on the ethics of such a rule rather than on an objective analysis of the situation. Unsound and wasteful proposals such as using returnable bottles under all conditions or sorting household trash before it is collected may well be motivated simply by the "waste not, want not" rule.

In Czechoslovakia, which is a highly industrialized country, some older rural folk still make their own soap from animal fats, mainly from the inedible parts of slaughtered pigs. They could buy many different kinds of toilet soap, perfumed and making rich lather, at the local store just like in America, and this is what most people do. But many of the older folk still make stuff which does not have a pleasant odor, makes little lather, and in general the only thing it shares with modern soap is its basic molecular structure, which is such that it enables dirt to coagulate and to be rinsed away. It takes hours of unpleasant, smelly and messy processing to produce the stuff, and when the goo has solidified in cardboard boxes, it must be cut into bars and ground into flakes for washing the laundry. And all this instead of a trip to the store and a little money for good and pleasant toilet soap. It is not so much that they do it because their mothers did it, and their grandmothers before them; it is that when they slaughter a pig, they cannot bring themselves to throw out any part of it unused: "Waste not, want not." It never occurs to them that they are wasting hours of time that they could have spent reading a good book or playing a game of chess. It never occurs to them that time is worth more than money, for lost money may be regained, but lost time is gone forever. They waste not, but they want.

America has been, and still is, on a binge of waste making that makes the rest of the world gasp. But to flip into the opposite extreme of separating used toothpicks from used toothpaste tubes in every household ultimately means more waste still.

This chapter has attempted to rebut some of the myths disseminated by the imploitation nuts, and from these rebuttals alone, it might seem that there is nothing to worry about. But this is not so. A look at the barrels of empty oil cans that are collected from all the gas stations in the U.S.A. every week to be buried in land fills is enough to make every sane man shudder, and half a ton of paper per family per year, if nothing else, is ultimately robbing that family of more valuable things. I will readily concede that the environmentalists, no matter how fanatical, have done a good thing in drawing public attention to such wastes. Unfortunately, they did not leave it at that, and they are now burying the real issues under mountains of hysterics and technophobia. Recycled paper, for example, is a costly and inferior product; on the other hand, recycled oil is often a better lubricant than freshly refined oil.

This book does not plead for replacing one kind of extremism by another; it merely pleads for reason and sanity.

4

More Power Means More Pollution: More Doctors Mean More Disease

All power pollutes.
Garrett De Bell

We insist and will continue to insist that the only answer is to use less power.
Thomas Turner

Environmental Handbook, Ballantine Books, New York, 1970.

There are three basic approaches to the problem of pollution in any form: Clean-up of sites that are polluted already, removal of pollutants at their source, and prevention of pollution by substituting non-polluting equipment for the sources of pollution. None of these three approaches can be accomplished without power, which in practice means electric power. But the fact is that the United States, with by far the highest amount of power generation of any country in the world (both total and per capita), does not have enough electric power to tackle the first of these three approaches without drastic curbs of supplying power to other needs, it may only scrape through with enough power to realize the second approach, and it is not, in the near future, able to realize the third approach, in part because of insufficient vigor in pursuing research of pollutionless power generation, in part because of the legalistic guerilla tactics by environmental organizations which are delaying and preventing cleaner methods of power generation.

Regulate the demand for more electric power is the simplistic solution of the simplifiers. Among many other things, they overlook that pollution control is one of the substantial creators of demand for more electric power. Then take the power from "somewhere else," they say, often pointing to the electric toothbrush, which in recent years has come to be the symbol of a gadget-loving society that wastes too much power. Whilst personally I, too, think that an electric toothbrush is a somewhat ridiculous appliance, the fact is that if every inhabitant of the United States owned an electric tooth-brush and every one of them, including breast-fed infants and tooth-less old men, used it three times a day, then in a month of such monumental electric tooth cleaning the entire population would not use up the electric energy that was expended in the printing and binding of a single environmental bestseller.

There is, of course, very much waste of electric power, and by bigger loads than toothbrushes. But there are also virtually limitless supplies of energy that can be harnessed and converted to electric power, and without pollution. But apart from other considerations, the technophobes who hope to cut the demand for industrial electric power are in for a surprise, should the power supply be unable to cope with demand.

The domestic and residential power consumption now amounts to more than half of the power consumed by industry and commerce (which also includes sewage plants, water pumping stations, schools, hospitals, and a hundred other "good" uses). So where is the needed power going to come from? From the steel plants that make scrubbers to keep pollutants out of the stack? From the chemical plants that provide the raw materials for filtering of pollutants? From hospitals? From the telephone network? You can switch off a few pinball machines and illuminated advertisements, but in the end you will have to do what every government, totalitarian or democratic, has done when the country ran out of power: Switch off the residential districts, for that is where most power can be saved with the least serious consequences. In the long run, the least important and hungriest power consumer is your kitchen range, your heat and your light. When the power is switched off in a section of a Russian city, they switch off the residential districts without asking the residents; but neither does the British government go to the country with a plebiscite when the miners strike. Like their Soviet colleagues, they switch off the "non-essential" power, which means the power that heats and lights homes. It is unrealistic to fantasize about a population submitting to blackouts voluntarily. For people in America are basically not different from those in Britain or Russia: If pollution alerts or power shortages requires power to be switched around, then let us switch it around, by all means; but let me be on the board that does the switching.

Borrowing from Peter to pay Paul has a habit of leaving both Peter and Paul without money. Depriving people of electric power will not stop them coughing from the smog, but it will make them cough from pneumonia as well. It is not only unrealistic to expect people to curb their power consumption, but it is also insolent. For nature has given us such an abundant supply of energy to be harnessed that a power shortage in an industrialized country cannot be caused by anything but ignorance, mismanagement or mischief. With the exception of natural disasters and war, no industrial country has ever run out of power for any other reason. If the United States runs out of power, and this is a very real possibility, then it will not be due to lack of natural energy, but to lack of foresight in preparing the necessary technology. The power supplies will have dried up not because they were wrecked by the toothbrushes, but because they were wrecked by the technophobia preached by the professors of apocalyptic holocaustology. Pollution is not curbed by sterilizing the population and exterminating its diabetics, but by the scrubbers, filters and treatment plants that run on electricity.*

THE foreseeable future does not bode a better form of energy for distribution from a central source than electric energy; and it is virtually certain that central stations of energy conversion will remain with us far into the future, for a central large convertor can always be made more efficient than a large number of small ones. There are several reasons why electricity is the most attractive form of generating and distributing energy. It is, for one thing, more easily controlled than any other form of power. The butterfly throttle linked to the accelerator pedal of a car, for example, controls the power available from the engine; but it is a pretty crude affair, and it can

---

* Since the above was written, the first blackouts due to insufficient power hit New York; Queens and Brooklyn were switched off during a heat wave in July 1972. Not only were air conditioners useless, but hundreds of tons of food were spoiled without refrigeration. Large areas of the north east were blanketed by aggravated air pollution at the same time. The environmentalists, who had prevented the construction of nuclear power stations by their legal suits, were calling for more suits against Con Edison for switching off the power.

only be used within certain limits. An entirely different mechanism, the brakes, must be brought into play to reduce the kinetic energy of the car by changing it into heat in the brake linings, which is a pretty crude affair of controlling the energy flow, too. In a small energy convertor like a car, this is good enough, because it does not handle much energy anyway. But in a diesel-electric engine of a train, for example, it is considered worthwhile to sacrifice a little energy in the conversion from the kinetic energy produced by the diesel engine to the electric energy produced by a generator, in order to give better control of the available power.

Another reason that makes electric power superior to other forms of energy is the ease of its transmission. With the possible exception of future electromagnetic beams, there is nothing in sight that can handle the vast flows of energy with the same small losses, small dimensions, cleanliness and speed (of restoring interrupted flow) of an electric transmission line.

There are other reasons, but the one of interest here is the total absence of pollution in the generation of electric power *as such*; this may sound paradoxical, but pollution never arises in the conversion stage where energy is actually converted to to electric power, it arises in the preceding steps of energy conversion, in particular, in some forms of converting the heat released by fuel into the kinetic energy of the machines (such as steam turbines) driving the electric generators. No pollution whatever is generated in converting that kinetic energy into electric power.* Electric power is absolutely clean, even if some processes now in use, but not physically essential, pollute in the preliminary stages of its generation.

Electric energy can be gained directly from almost any other form of energy, but in many cases this can only be done on a small scale. For example, heat can be converted directly into electricity by heating a thermocouple (the joint of two different metals), but the power obtainable from the ends of the two metal conductors is usually not more than required to move the needle of a measuring instrument. (There are some interesting, if unimportant, exceptions to this statement. The Russians have constructed an appliance in the form of a kerosene lamp whose heat warms a large battery of thermocouples arranged round the circumference of the lamp. This provides the power supply for a radio receiver built into the lamp, and enables

---

* Power, strictly speaking, is the *rate* at which energy is produced or consumed, but the distinction is blurred in loose language, where it is usual to talk about kinetic *energy* and electric *power*. This is a peculiarity of English; other languages use the equivalent of *power* only when required by its rigorous definition.

Siberians, far from the power net and cut off from supplies of batteries by the long winter, to listen to the radio by utilizing the heat of a light source.) Similarly, chemical energy can be turned directly into electric power by the cells of an electric battery, and conversions from light, radioactive radiation, sound and other forms of energy are also possible; however, at present, the only form of energy that can be converted into electric power directly and on a very large scale is kinetic energy, most often that of a rotating turbine, driven either by steam or by water.

Hydraulic turbines driving electric generators are perhaps the best proof that electric power is totally clean and that the pollution unleashed in its generation is due to the particular preliminary processes generating kinetic, not electric, energy. The kinetic energy of the water driving the turbines of a hydroelectric plant comes directly from the sun, which lifts the water from the oceans, and from the earth's gravitation, which supplies the other part of the energy needed to keep the water in circulation and to drive the hydraulic turbines.

The kinetic energy of flowing water is determined not only by its velocity, but also by its quantity, and a lazily flowing river may have much more kinetic energy than a swiftly flowing stream; however, to utilize a hydraulic turbine efficiently, the velocity of the water must be high, and the most common method of harnessing water power is to build a dam and to run the turbines from the water falling through a pipe (the penstock). A dam also has additional benefits in providing flood control, water storage, and recreational facilities.

Only about 16% of the electric power generated and consumed in the United States now comes from hydroelectric plants (not counting pumped storage). In part, this is due to the geographic characteristics of the country; hydroelectric dams can easily be built only in mountainous or hilly country. However, the possibilities of harnessing the energy of flowing water are far from exhausted. The many advantages of hydroelectric plants include the total absence of pollution and the fact that the technology is entirely ready. Add to this that the input energy comes free of charge, does not involve any transportation of fuels (as is the case with fuel burning and present nuclear plants), and does not use up an ounce of resources, and you would expect that people who know no other criteria than clean-up of pollution, freedom from further pollution and resource conservation would clamor for more hydroelectric plants. But if there are people who have only such issues at heart, they are not making themselves heard. The motely crowd of resource conservers and anti-pollution crusaders raise a furor every time a hydroelectric dam is proposed. Bankrupt of arguments where resources and pollution are concerned, they pull "visual pollution" out of their bottomless arsenal of catch phrases, though not even this argument will hold water. Quite apart from the fact that many people consider an artificial lake no more ugly than a natural one (few can tell the difference without asking), there are sites for such plants that cannot now be reached by anything but terrain vehicles. Arizona, Nevada, Colorado, Utah and other mountain states have such places. One of these, a remote and inaccessible part of the Grand Canyon in Arizona, was proposed as such a site. But a furor of "Save the Grand Canyon!" went up. If the Grand Canyon had really been threatened, one must suppose the catch phrase would have been "Save the Solar System." The fact that many more Americans go to see the urban areas of Europe than the beauties of Grand Canyon is a side thought which I will not go into, mainly because it is nobody's business how a family spend their vacations. The point to be made is that not even "visual pollution" is an argument that will stand up to the facts where hydroelectric plants are concerned, and it is totally shattered when the alternatives are considered. Saving a few hidden nooks and crannies in the mountains or the semi-deserts will multiply the pressures for power stations whose pollution must often be curbed by complicated methods, and whose input energy involves more transportation, more pollution, and more depletion. Hydroelectric plants are clean and the energy comes to their sites free of any cost in money or adverse side effects.

Among the countries that have effectively harnessed the clean energy of flowing water are Sweden, and to a lesser extent, Switzerland. The hydroelectric plants of those countries have not driven the tourists away. In the case of Sweden, they have helped to make the country second only to the United States in per capita consumption of electric power. But it is not the hydroelectric plants that cause pollution in Sweden; it is the raw sewage dumped into the Baltic in Leningrad which washes onto the beaches in Stockholm. The large power consumption in Sweden, which is one of the cleanest industrialized countries in the world, is partly due to its production of electrosteel, for Sweden is also the second largest producer of steel per capita. In fact, Sweden must be the country Paul Ehrlich has in mind when he measures impact on the environment by a country's steel production, and pollution by its power consumption. Though his arguments are equally profound when thermal generation of power is considered, I insert them here, because in my opinion this is the place where Ehrlich has outdone himself: "The birth of every American baby is roughly fifty times the stress on the environment of this planet as the birth of every Indian baby. This estimate is based on power consumption figures, which are an excellent measure of the degree of pollution. The birth of every American baby puts roughly three hundred times the demand on the nonrenewable materials of this planet as the birth of every Indonesian baby (based on per capita steel consumption figures)."*

Why stop there, Dr. Ehrlich? I would estimate this birth-to-bugaboo ratio to be in the millions for Malaysian babies, when the comparison is based on the per capita purchase of baseball tickets, and the situation becomes even more frightening for Eskimo babies, when the ratio is based on the pounds of pop corn sold in drive-in cinemas. But let us be fair to American babies, who are not the worst offenders. The real villains of this world are the kids of Nepal. This estimate is based on the per capita altitude above sea level.

But let us return to more serious matters. The conversion of kinetic to electric energy is not only totally free of pollution, it is also one of the most efficient known to the present state of technology. The efficiency of conversion from kinetic to electric energy, or vice versa, can be made as high as 98% without extraordinary difficulties, only 2% being lost as heat in the conversion. This is a value unparalleled in any other presently used large-scale energy conversion. For example, the heat generated by combustible fuels to the kinetic energy of a steam turbine only rarely reaches 47% (quite often it is as low as 30%), and the efficiency of the internal combustion engine is usually below 25%. The efficiency of a light bulb, as noted earlier, is only 10% or less, though this is not, of course, conversion on a large scale. Moreover, in many cases the same convertor can be used for conversion of kinetic to electric energy and for conversion in the opposite direction. A DC motor, for example, will rotate when current flows through its windings, and it can be used as a generator of current when its armature (core) is rotated.

These properties of kinetic-electric energy conversion can be put to good use in the generation and storage of electric power. One of the frustrations of supplying the demand for electric power is the unevenness of that demand. Most power is needed during the peak

---

* *The Population Crisis: Where We Stand.* Bibliographic data on p. 64.

hour, which now usually occurs round noon or the early afternoon, and a power station may not have enough to supply it; but at about 3 to 4 a.m., a power station has more than enough power, but few people need it. In a thermal power station, the fire under the boilers cannot be extinguished at night and lit again in the morning; but neither will a hydroelectric plant gain much by shutting off its penstock to let the water rise in the reservoir behind the dam, for the reservoir is large in area (or it would not be a reservoir) and the water flowing in during the night will not raise the level appreciably. Yet it is the difference in water levels that determines the velocity of the water transferring (some of) its kinetic energy to the blades of the hydraulic turbine. A very simple solution of this problem of conserving the unwanted energy during the night for use during the peak hours came into use in Europe in the 1930's. The power generated during the night is used to pump water into a higher reservoir (up to about 1,700 feet higher), and the water is allowed to flow out again and through the turbines during the peak hours. Some power is, of course, wasted as heat in the motors and pumps and in friction of the water flowing through the pipes, in fact, the whole arrangement is usually not more than 72% efficient, and in some cases the efficiency is as low as 50%. However, efficiency is not very relevant here, since the useful energy comes out of an amount that would otherwise be lost anyway. In any case, this simple method will adapt the available power to the fluctuations of the demand for it.

This simple, and in itself pollutionless, method of storing power to satisfy the demand of peak hours is beginning to be used on very large scales in America. Pumped storage facilities are in operation in Pennsylvania, Arizona, California, Oklahoma and other states. The capacity of such plants has increased from 677 megawatts in 1963 to almost ten times that amount at present, and further facilities with a total of many thousands of megawatts are now under construction.

A giant plant using pumped storage is now under construction near Ludington, Michigan. It uses six reversible turbines (which can act either as pumps when turned by electric power, or as turbines when turned by water flowing in the opposite direction) to pump water from Lake Michigan into a 27 billion gallon reservoir at a height 300 feet above its level; when the peak demand requires the potential energy of this reservoir to be turned into electric power, the water will rush through six giant penstocks 24 to 28 feet in diameter at the rate of 34 million gallons a minute and turn the reversible turbines, the biggest ever made. They will generate 1900 megawatts of power to keep the presses of the technophobes running. The entire project will be completed in 1973, and a pumped storage plant with a three times greater output is planned for construction near Arcadia, Michigan, in the 1980's.

There is an essential difference between these plants on the shores of Lake Michigan and a hydroelectric power plant using this method. If the electric power activating the pumps comes itself from hydraulic power, the only pollution created is that coming out of the pipe of the chief engineer. On the other hand, if the pumps are run on power generated in fuel burning power stations, as is now the case for the plants in Michigan, the process is not free of pollution. In fact, since the pumps of the Michigan pumped storage plant will consume more power than is generated by the reverse flow of the water (for the same reasons as given in the case of hydroelectric stations) it might seem that the whole idea only creates more pollution still, and I can well imagine that the Michigan chapter of the Friends of the Earth is trying to make something out of that point. But this is not so. There are at least three points which such an argument would overlook.

First, the presently used methods of supplying peak demands create a disproportionate amount of pollution. There are few linear systems in the world, and the pollution produced by a fossil-burning power plant increases faster as the power output approaches capacity and overload conditions. Though it is not a natural law, it is a tendency supported by widely ranging experience that systems of all types run less reliably and less efficiently when pushed to the limits of their capacity. Certainly this is true of a power plant. For example, the additionally needed heat must be prepared well ahead of the peak hour, and it does not die down immediately when the peak hours are over. (In contrast, when the steel gates of the Michigan pumped storage plant are opened, the power output rises from zero to 1900 megawatts in three minutes.) A power station, just like a car, consumes more fuel per unit available power when it is working at overload than when it is supplying power well below its capacity. For example, the wonderful "average" miles per gallon extolled by the automobile advertisements are averaged in flat terrain at cruising speed. No sane publicity department of an automobile company will measure the gas mileage of its cars when they are going over the Continental Divide or racing at 100 miles an hour across the salt flats. Only Ford had a better idea: A Maverick was shown above the caption "From zero to 60 m.p.h. for under 5 cents." Take paper and pencil and estimate the gas mileage: If the acceleration is not shamefully weak, they are telling us that for a nickle's worth of capacity power, one can make a car guzzle gas at the rate of something like one mile to the gallon.

Second, most power plants have stand-by turbines which are brought in to tackle the peak hour demand. These turbines run for only a few hours a day and often on special fuels. These units are generally not the ones where all the pollution controls are concentrated. A plant of the Michigan type, even if at present the pumps run on thermally generated power, raises the overall efficiency of power generation during the peak hours, among other things, to activate the pollution controls. And it is precisely during the peak hours that these controls are most urgently in need of power.

Third, the power that runs the Michigan storage plant is supplied by thermal power stations at present, and only as a matter of necessity, not as a matter of principle. This power will eventually come from nuclear power stations, whose thermal pollution is a sorry joke, and whose radioactive wastes can be rendered harmless. The only ones who are delaying the construction of nuclear power stations are the ones that cause the builders to be hit by injunction after injunction on the grounds that there is too much pollution.

All of these points, of course, are irrelevant where the storage of the potential energy of the water is accomplished by hydroelectric plants.

Consider next the "thermal" power stations which now generate the majority (about three quarters) of the electric power consumed in the United States. The term "thermal" is a misnomer, because nuclear power plants are no less thermal than the "thermal" stations; they simply produce the heat in a different way, namely by nuclear reactions rather than by chemical ones (burning). The energetic efficiency of fuel burning power stations is low, and they pollute. Though only about 2% of the kinetic energy of the steam (or other) turbines is lost as heat in the generators changing kinetic to electric energy, some 60 to 70% of the chemical energy stored in the fuel goes out through the stack with the hot gases and pollutants before the fuel heat is converted into the kinetic energy of the turbines. Certainly this is not a good system, and it should be replaced. But the present power plants cannot be replaced overnight, least of all in the face of the opposition of the instant environ-

cooling tower *stacks* *cooling tower*

Not all pollution is visible, and not everything visible pollutes. The thick white stuff coming out of the cooling towers (when the dew point is low) is harmless water vapor; the toxic gases coming out of the stacks are invisible.

mentalists and de-developers, who shout "pollution!" most loudly when something is being done to combat the roots of pollution and not just its symptoms.

Before discussing what can be done, let us take a quick look at what should not be done. There is, for example, the instant expert who measures the pollution by the local power plant by the amounts of white smoke that he sees rising from it. At times this smoke comes out ominously thick and rises to great heights above the plant. It is then that the instant expert shouts most loudly about the apalling state of affairs, and if he sees the big white cloud from a bus as it approaches a distant city in the valley below (which makes the picture look particularly ominous), he will unfailingly secure the co-disapproval and shocked indignation of the other passengers. But if the instant expert took another look, he would see that the white stuff is not coming out of the stacks, but out of the cooling towers. It is as harmless as the white clouds in the sky, for it is, in fact, the same thing: water vapor condensing in cooler air. The steam that drives the turbines is not only pushed into them by the high pressure from the boilers, it is also sucked out of them by the low pressure produced in the condensers, where the steam condenses into the water that circulates back again into the water tubes of the boilers.

These condensers must be cooled by water, and this water, in turn, is cooled by drizzling in small drops through the cooling towers (sometimes wooden pyramids, but most often concrete structures in the shape of a hyperboloid, see photo on p. 113), and it is from the open top of the cooling towers that the water vapor emerges and condenses in the cooler layers of air above. How big and ominous the resultant cloud looks is not determined by the pollutants (it does not have any), but by the temperature and humidity of the atmosphere on that day. On the other hand, many pollutants are invisible, and they therefore do not bother the instant expert.

The instant expert and his measurement of pollution by looking out of the window of a running bus does, however, remind one of another predicament, and that is that there is at present no fully reliable and accurate method of measuring the rates at which different pollutants are discharged into the air from a stack. Very simple, says the instant expert. Electronic sensors! And he looks at you with an expression demanding the Nobel prize. Yes, electronic sensors are both reliable and accurate; but not in the heat and smoke of a stack. New measurement methods need research, funds, skilled scientists, labs and equipment, not de-development and nonsensical talk about power consumption being an excellent measure of pollution.

Another brilliant scheme proposed by the instant experts is to switch to gas, which will rid the atmosphere of the pollution by power plants. It will do no such thing; it will increase the overall pollution. It is true that gas does not have some of the pollutants which are thrown into the air by burning coal, especially high-sulfur content coal; but if there were no more to it, then the problem would be much more easily solved by switching the power plants from coal to natural gas (which many of them are burning anyway). Quite apart from the fact that the United States is already short of natural gas and is now importing large quantities in liquid form from overseas, the main point is that ten thousand small fires create more pollution than one big one, because a much larger fraction of the total energy goes out of the chimney of a home than out of the stack of a power station. The ten thousand little fires make more smoke than the single big one.

The opposite argument is only slightly less fallacious. For example, those who see the electric car as a cure-all of air pollution think only of the missing exhaust of the car; they forget about the stack of the power station that will be overloaded by the demand to charge all those batteries. It is true that a substantial improvement in air quality could be achieved by the electric car; but unless the power stations are modernized too, the electric car will not eliminate air pollution.

These are some examples of what cannot be done. Now what *can* be done? The immediate thing that can be done is to patch up a bad system, since it cannot be thrown out straight away. The example of Britain shows that this can be done, for the great majority of British power plants is also still non-nuclear; yet industrial air pollution has been very substantially curbed in Britain even if it cannot be eliminated totally when the root of the problem is still present. Of course, the British started on pollution control (or "smoke abatement" in British usage) in the early fifties, which gave them the considerable advantage of getting on with it before they were bedeviled by the various priests of the ecocult, with which they now seem no less stricken than Americans. In fact, the American crusaders who shot down the SST gobbled up hungrily every one of the horror stories with which their British fellow crusaders have been trying to shoot down the Concorde for years. But that is another matter; the fact is that London fogs have been eliminated, and the average Londoner's life has been demonstrably prolonged. Whatever germs thrived in London fogs have been stamped out from the ecosystem by the ruthless selfishness of the British who considered the lives of human beings more important.

There are two basic approaches to curbing the pollution generated by a fuel burning power plant. One is to use fuels with a minimum of pollutants, the other is to remove those pollutants from the stack before they are emitted into the air. Unfortunately, the minimum of pollutants that can reasonably be achieved by burning the right kinds of fuels is still quite large, and it cannot be reduced to zero by the scrubbers that filter out the pollutants. Both approaches are simply patch-ups of an unsatisfactory system. However, in the immediate future there is no other choice (where fossil-burning plants are concerned), and the best available method cannot be condemned on the grounds that it is not perfect. But let it not be forgotten that both methods are, indeed, imperfect and neither represents a permanent solution.

The usual problems of patch-ups are met in this as in other cases: The patch is stronger than the material of the pants underneath it, and sooner or later the patch tears new holes into the pants. The two most usual types of pollution control equipment are the centrifugal

scrubber and the electrostatic preciptator. The heart of the centrifugal scrubber is a chamber in which the smoke and gases resulting
from combustion are forced into an eddy-like spiral motion. The
centrifugal force on the particulate pollutants pushes them to the
outer circumference of the eddy, where they can be separated from
the lighter gases and scrubbed by water jets. The electrostatic precipitator is a long rod under high voltage located in the center of a
vertical chamber. An electric charge is induced in the particles of the
fly ash, and electrostatic forces attract the fly ash to the rod, where it
precipitates. The heavy accumulation of fly ash on the rod can then
be disposed of, for example, by mechanical impact, which will cause
it to fall down into a depository.

But the electrostatic precipitator works better catching the fly ash
of high sulfur coal than that of low-sulfur coal, which has less
pollutants and is now more widely used. The nitrogen oxides generated in high-temperature combustion are caught by neither method,
and they are generated in the combustion of natural gas as well as in
the combustion of coal; they are one of the contributors to photo-
chemical smog. For nitrogen oxides, a quite different technology is
required, one that is as yet largely undeveloped. The Pacific Gas and
Electric Company has started experimenting with such a technology,
and has attained partial success. But the cost per generating unit
was $600,000. The shoddy fabric of the pants is being patched up
with patches of gold. Note that I am not talking about the costs and
methods of pollution clean-up throughout the country. I am not, for
example, talking about the costs and methods of cleaning up such
industries as cement, leather tanning, metals smelting, vegetable
canning, steel making, iron foundries, petroleum refinieries or pulp
and paper mills, let alone cleaning up Lake Erie. I am only talking
about the methods and costs of the very first step: cleaning up the
cleaner, that is, controlling pollution by the power stations, which
will have to supply the bulk of the energy needed for pollution control everywhere else. Electric power, presented by the Ehrlichs and
De Bells as the Big Polluter, is in fact the doctor that will have to
cure the disease.

And it is right that costs should be considered, for at this stage,
the entire affair becomes less technical and more economic. The
power industry expects to spend $500 billion over the next 20 years
to build 300 new power plants to supply the power needs predicted
by the Federal Power Commision and conforming to the tough air
quality standards that will go into effect in 1975. The Council of

Environmental Quality (a government agency) estimates antipollution spending at $287 billion over the next 10 years. That is about $1,500 per inhabitant of the United States. Remember the 15 cents for the researchers of the US Bureau of Mines (p. 98)? They never got the 15 cents; they got fifteen hundredths of one penny. Solar energy and MHD research was, and is, starved of funds, too; they come under the space research that has been decimated by the Neo-Luddites. Being penny-wise with scientific research has never yet produced anything but dollar foolishness. But it is too late now; the price will have to be paid, and it will go nowhere but up if we listen to the technophobes. Since it has to be paid anyway, it might as well be spent prudently.

When one's pants begin to fall apart, one can patch them up, or get a new pair, or go without pants. I know of no fourth way. Going without pants is what the de-developers propose. But they will not be able to persuade anybody to go without power or the other amenities of modern life. They are not even taking such proposals seriously themselves. Mrs. Econut may have thrown out her electric tooth brush, but she has not thrown out the kitchen range. And she has not yet been seen beating the wash with a bat on a stone in her heated swimming pool. (I may have started a new subcult there.) So let us waste no more time on such wisdom.

Patching up the pants is necessary when no new pants are available. But in the long run the patches will not save the pants either. The patches will tear new holes in the shoddy fabric, and when the patches start costing more than a new pair of pants, it is a reliable indication that the time for stop-gap measures is long past. A prudent pant wearer uses patches only for the time that he is weaving the fabric for new pants.

That is the situation with pollution control. The presently used and proposed measures, when all is said and done, consist in creating pollution and then getting rid of it again. There is no other choice this year or next year, and the system is not hopeless; it is certainly better than creating pollution and doing nothing about it. But no housewife pushes the dirt around with a dirty broom, and the first thing to do for a long range solution is to clean up the cleaner, that is, rid the power stations of pollution, not because they create more pollution than anything else (it was not the power stations that polluted Lake Erie), but because they will have to supply the power for the scrubbers, the water treatment plants, and for the demands of pollution control technology in the mines, the chemical industry, the paper industry, the steel industry and in all other fields containing sources of pollution. The power needed to do this job is no joke; it is always overlooked by those who oppose power plants because they pollute. 20 million tons of sulfur dioxide a year are now being spewed into the air by coal burning plants — not only power plants, but smelters, refineries and many other industrial plants. One possibility of cleaning them out of the smoke is to scrub the sulfur oxides with limestone. But the process creates mountains of calcium sulfate, another potential pollutant, and to dispose of it involves further processing plants. What are they going to run on? A tread mill? Oxen fed on organically grown foods? And the sulfur oxides problem is as nothing compared to cleaning up Lake Erie. Obviously, the first step in a long range solution must be to clean up the power plants, or the dirt will simply be pushed around with a dirty broom.

But the patches are becoming more costly than the pants. Scrubbers, precipitators and other means of pollution control represent not only great sums of capital investments, but also in operating costs. Some steel plants already spend twice as much on the maintenance of air pollution controls as on that of steel making tools — and they still pollute. I am not asking you to break down in tears over the money the steel companies lose. I am asking you to consider how much sense it makes to sink billions into stop-gap equipment and technologies that won't do the job properly. As far as the $287 billion for environmental clean up are concerned, "internalizing costs" and other fancy names only amount to saying that the big companies will *advance* the money, but they will eventually get it back from you and me. You can fool some of the people some of the time, but in the end all the people pay all the bills. The companies who pay $60,000 a minute to advertise their products on television are only advancing the money, too; we pay it back to them when we buy their products, in fact, we pay them enough extra so that they can finance campaigns against "paid" television. In any case, I would think that common sense dictates sinking the big money into the new pants, and not the patches. What is needed right now are the patches in the form of scrubbers and precipitators, yes; but only enough to scrape through until the new pants are ready — the nuclear power plants that do not need any patches. They do not need scrubbers because they do not even have stacks.

The presently running nuclear power plants do not differ from combustion plants very radically. The system of steam turbines and generators is the same as before; but the heat needed to turn water into steam is supplied by nuclear reactions rather than by the chemical reaction of combustion. There are no airborne pollutants produced in the process. The cost of nuclear power is still high, but it will inevitably come down as the technology spreads and develops. Only a decade ago, the cost of computers was in the millions. You can now buy a little calculator using the same principles as a computer for under $100; it does as much as a $800 desk calculator, only faster, and it is pocket sized. Within one or two years one can reasonably expect its price to be substantially lowered in spite of inflation, but the interesting point is this: The main cost is the display, the keyboard and the other orthodox peripherals — the heart of the calculator, the chips that do the actual computing, are almost a free gift attached to these auxiliaries. (The comparison with computers involves the lowered cost of the chips, the price of the same computer has not gone down from millions to $100.) All technologies have gone this way, and there is no reason to think that nuclear power generation will be different. The fact that nuclear power is now more expensive per kilowatt-hour than power produced from coal does not mean a thing; in fact, the statement is not even true when the overall costs paid by society are considered.

Nuclear energy is liberated as heat and other forms by converting mass into energy. There is hardly a science fiction show that does not include the obligatory equation $E = mc^2$, but the statement "mass is turned into energy" may be misleading. If *all* the mass of an atomic bomb could be turned into energy, then the contemporary megaton bombs would be as a fly's sneeze compared to it. In fact, only a very minute fraction of the total mass is turned into energy. When the nucleus of an atom is split into its component particles, the sum of the masses of the individual particles is not exactly the same as the mass of the original nucleus when it was still in one piece. The small difference between the two masses is what is liberated as energy in accordance with the well known formula; the main part was mass before the reaction and it remains mass after it. The difference between the mass of a nucleus and the mass of its component particles may be either an excess or a defect. At the end of the periodic table of chemical elements (high atomic numbers), e.g., for uranium and plutonium, the difference is a mass *defect*; the nucleus has more mass than its component particles, and it must therefore be split to gain energy. At the opposite end of the table (low atomic numbers), e.g., for hydrogen and helium, the difference is an excess, and to gain energy, the particles must be fused into new nuclei, which is done both in the sun and in the hydrogen bomb by raising the temperature sufficiently high; the resulting fusions will then keep the temperature high enough to keep a chain reaction going.

The continuous flow of energy from nuclear fuel requires a self-sustaining chain reaction. If the process is one that is based on the fission of the nuclei, as it is for uranium and plutonium, the chain reaction sustains itself because, to cut a long story short, the particles flying out of one nucleus will break up other nuclei, though most of them, in a power generating reactor, enter a material called the moderator. The difference between the atomic bomb and the reaction liberating heat for a power plant is that in the former case the available energy is let loose in a fraction of a second, whereas in a power generating reactor the chain reaction is slow and controlled.

And this brings me to a widespread fear, and widespread not only among the ecocult; the fear is that controlled reaction will get out of control and result in an atomic explosion. The technophobes have pictured every nuclear power plant as a potential atomic bomb, and they have played cleverly on the association of "atomic" and "bomb." Such fears are totally groundless, for the construction for producing an explosive chain reaction rather than a controlled one is entirely different in character, it is not merely a difference in degree. To produce an atomic explosion is not as easy as setting a match to an ammunition dump. It took the world's most brilliant scientists, including Albert Einstein, Enrico Fermi, Niels Bohr and many other stars of the scientific world to find the means of producing an explosive chain reaction, and they found it only long after they had found the means of producing the slow reaction that takes place in an atomic reactor. The night watchman of a power plant is not likely to stumble onto it by mistake. Even a scientist who is both brilliant and vicious could no more steal into a power plant and quickly make an atomic bomb out of the plutonium used in a reactor than he could steal into an office to make gun powder out of the typewriters.

A more probable among the improbabilities is the melting of the core of a nuclear reactor. The plutonium or uranium rods produce more heat than can be utilized for producing the steam to drive the turbogenerators, and they must therefore be cooled. Should the cooling system fail, the heat would increase to an extent where any metal container would melt and the power plant would spew forth a lethal cloud of radioactive particles. But when danger is concentrated at one point only, safety measures bordering on the absurd can be implemented to reduce the probability of the danger to almost zero. Bacteriological warfare research, for example, was such a case of immense dangers whose source was concentrated at a single or at a few points in the country. In 25 years of playing with this far more lethal danger, the only victims were some 150 sheep in Utah. The gold of Fort Knox has never yet been stolen, and it is more difficult to take countermeasures against planned damage than against accidental damage. Mechanical failure in the rapidly spinning turbogeberators of present power plants would make the machine fly apart with the force of a dynamite explosion; but this does not happen. The elevators in skyscrapers do not plunge down the shaft by accidental rupture of the suspension cables. Yet a nuclear power plant can be protected against the eventuality of the core melting by an incomparably higher safety factor than is the case for elevator riders plunging to their deaths.

Why, then, will nobody give a guarantee that a nuclear plant will never melt its core and spew forth a radioactive cloud? For the same reason that nobody will give a guarantee that a Pulitzer prize winner will never be stamped to death by an elephant ridden by one-eyed twins. A chance in a billion is not zero.

But apart from the general evils of technology, we are being scared by two more bugaboos: thermal pollution and the hazards of radioactive wastes.

Thermal pollution means different things to different environmentalists, but the majority understands it to mean the warming up of rivers and lakes by the excess heat dissipated by nuclear power plants, and the resulting interference with aquatic wildlife. Such warming of rivers and lakes can, of course, be prevented if it is considered worthwhile. The excess heat, that is, the heat not converted to kinetic energy of the turbines, need not be dissipated in rivers, it can be dissipated in artificial lakes or in the same type of cooling towers as are now used to dissipate the heat generated in the condensers of a combustion power plant which has no nearby river to do that job. There are no technical problems involved in that well known procedure.

The very fact that such a problem should arise is a convincing illustration of how superior nuclear power plants are in comparison with combustion plants: We are no longer worried about air pollution (which nuclear plants do not produce), but what the heat will do to aquatic wildlife. The point also illustrates the attitude of the fanatical environmentalists: Confronted with evidence that power can be generated without producing the pollutants that kill people, they fall back onto the argument that the alternative may harm aquatic wildlife; they are opposed to *all* technology, and it matters little to them whether it kills people or amoebae. In fact, if we judge the environmental fanatics by their deeds rather than their words, if we observe how they support the poorly performing pollution controls of combustion plants whilst doggedly opposing the slightest progress in constructing nuclear plants, we must conclude that they are more concerned about the health of amoebae than about that of human beings. We are back to the ever present undercurrent of the ecocult: Man is an unfortunate creation of nature.

It would be possible, therefore, at this point to say: Would you rather have people cough from filthy air, their eyes smart from the smog and their lives shortened by lung cancer and emphysema, or would you rather have a few species of fish die out or move elsewhere? However, it is my belief that the issue need not arise. I am not a biologist, and I may be quite wrong in what I am about to suggest, but in the extensive study that I made of the available literature on thermal pollution, I found nothing to convince me that thermal pollution of this type is anything but a shameless fraud. I repeat that the point is not essential, because the heat produced by a nuclear plant can be dissipated in artificial ponds or cooling towers, or it can be put to good use: Some of the uses that have been suggested include hot water supplies, special plant raising techniques (including the spraying of orchards with warm water when they are threatened by frost), and perhaps most important, evaporating sea water to gain fresh water. But here are my reasons for believing that "thermal pollution" is merely another red herring that has no foundation even if we accept the premise that man has no more right to life than an amoeba. Nature populates all of the landmasses of the globe with her species, and a considerable part of the oceans as well. The warm waters of the tropics support tropical fish, and the ice floes of the arctic support polar bears and penguins. If conditions change in some small part of the environment, and they change within small limits, one species moves out, and another moves in. Such changes occur in nature, and such changes are sometimes made by man. Man's activities support many species, and I do not mean domesticated animals and pets, but such species as the sparrow, who is found near man and his work; even the sea gull following a ship is a case in point. Man's agricultural activities gave more support to hamsters, field mice and a host of other species, whilst denying support to wolves, bears and a host of other species again. What kind of pollution is agriculture?

The heat dissipated in a river flowing past a nuclear power plant will not bring the water to a boil; it will raise it, depending on the quantity and the velocity of water, by a few degrees — only in exceptional cases by as much as 10° Centigrade. It therefore does not represent a drastic interference with nature such as virtually exterminating the buffalo or the whale or stamping out the bubonic plague or denying wolves a living. It will slightly shift the spectrum of species; it will deny some a living and it will give a living to others, as happened a thousand times before. We do not need any prejudice in favor of man to turn the environmental fanatic's own arguments against him: Why would you deny the species living in warmer water a living?

It is true that every energy conversion must give rise to heat, but to call this thermal "pollution" seems to make little more sense than pollution by double entry bookkeeping, which no doubt also accompanies every nuclear power plant. I believe that the issue of thermal pollution reveals the environmental fanatic for what he is: not a nature lover, but a technophobe. One does not have to accept my argument on shifting the biological spectrum of aquatic wildlife by a little higher temperature to see that this accusation is just. Not even the wildest econut would claim (one would hope) that nuclear power plants by the sea shore can significantly warm up the Atlantic or Pacific oceans. Yet environmental fanatics oppose nuclear power plants by the seaside as vehemently as plants cooled by rivers, and by their tactics of legalistic sabotage, they have been delaying their construction up to seven years. Who cares about wildlife? Who cares about pollution? Not the environmental fanatics; they are exclusively in the business of technophobia.

But should I be wrong on this point, it does not affect the essence of the issue. If there is such a thing as thermal pollution, it can easily be taken care of by a variety of methods, for example, by using the excess heat for desalination of sea water.

There is also the question of the atmosphere being warmed up by the heat generated in cooling towers and, for that matter, by any other industrial plant converting energy and by the many energy conversions taking place in a city. There is firm evidence that large cities, such as Los Angeles or New York, affect the local climate; the temperature of inner New York City, for example, is some 2° C higher than that in the surrounding rural areas. Does that matter?

Nobody knows. The thermal pollution panic is concerned with fish, not people, and once again the environmental fanatics have buried a more serious issue under their horror stories. At first sight, there seems to be no danger, because 2° C is much less than the day to day fluctuations in the same city, and much less than the difference between the average temperatures of Los Angeles and Phoenix, Arizona. The heat generated by a city is also utterly ridiculous compared with the energies (including heat) involved in the natural processes that take place in the atmosphere. Nevertheless, I am not prepared to dismiss a phenomenon that might affect people as lightly as the spectral shift of aquatic life in a river, which appears to be the more urgent concern of the environmentalists. But should this phenomenon prove serious, which does not seem very likely at present, then the obvious way to go is toward higher efficiencies in energy conversions and possibly to less concentration of industry; it still does not make a case for de-development, much less for catastrophe.

The radioactivity of the wastes of nuclear power stations, on the other hand, is not a fraud; the fission products of nuclear reactions are dangerously radioactive. However, unlike the pollutants of power stations working with combustible fuels, the radioactive wastes can be *totally* prevented from doing any harm. They do not fly out of the stack (there is none); they are in place, ready to be made ineffective. The amount of wastes is, compared to fossil-burning plants, quite small, for the radioactive fuel is processed and recycled after use before finally being disposed of. The final wastes are enclosed in leaden or concrete containers for shipment to disposal sites in geological formations where they can do no harm. The material of the container, incidentally, does not react with the wastes; it simply absorbs the radiation in thick walls of high density. "We are committing future generations to a problem that we do not know how to handle," says a British report referring to nuclear waste disposal. This is a statement that might equally well refer to burial of the dead in cemeteries. The Federal Power Commission Report (1970) says the following on this point: "Improvements in fuel technology and methods of reprocessing in the past ten years have reduced markedly the volume of high-activity wastes generated per unit power produced. The conversion of the high-level liquid wastes to stable solids, with subsequent long term storage or disposal in selected geological formations such as salt, has been demonstrated on an engineering scale. This technology, which has been developed during the past ten years, has provided the basis for a proposed

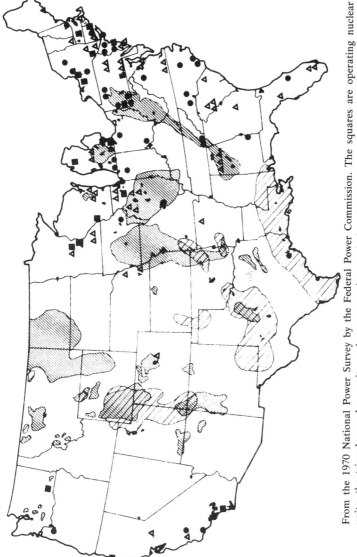

From the 1970 National Power Survey by the Federal Power Commission. The squares are operating nuclear units, the triangles nuclear units under construction, and the circular dots are ordered units. Most of the triangles and dots are constructions now delayed by the suits filed by environmental organizations. Whilst these non-polluting units are being held up, polluting plants run at top capacity. When they can no longer handle the load, many anti-pollution devices become inoperable, and tons of food rot in useless refrigerators.

Atomic Energy Commission policy on high level waste management. In this proposed policy, all high-activity waste from industrial fuel reprocessing will be solidified and transferred to a Federal Repository within ten years following separation of fission products from the irradiated fuel. When this policy is implemented, the levels of stored high level waste in liquid form are expected to be nominal."

But even conversion to solid form leaves an element of danger in handling them. In some respects, the situation is akin to the dangers of electric discharges in power stations and near transmission lines. There are some transmission lines whose voltage is much higher than that of the electric chair, but they are kept out of people's way where they cannot be normally dangerous. When electric power first appeared, people no doubt associated it with lightning, just as people today associate nuclear power with the atomic bomb. No one could at the time give them a guarantee that electricity would cause no fatal accident, and such fatal accidents did, in fact, occur. But today electric current is one of the rarest causes of accidental death. In the United States, the number of people killed by electric current is smaller than the number killed accidentally by poisoning, or drowning, or falling objects, or most other accidental causes (not to speak of such killers as automobile accidents, where the rate is more than 50 times higher). There will, no doubt, be accidents with radioactive materials; there may even be occasional major accidents, perhaps even disasters. But unlike fire, for example, radioactive materials are concentrated in only very few places and exclusively in the hands of experts, and even the major danger — transportation — can be controlled with exceptionally high safety measures. The probability of accidents is therefore much smaller than for accidents by fire — though admittedly the consequences of an accident may be more serious. A five-year old child can set a city ablaze, but it cannot, with reasonable probability, throw a pound of radioactive wastes into a city's water supply.

There is more than enough room to dispose of radioactive wastes below the biosphere, of whose narrowness we are constantly being reminded by the ecocult. Besides, nuclear power is not here to stay forever, either. Such processes as energy conversion directly from the sun's heat, MHD, or geothermal sources (to be discussed later) produce no radioactive wastes. But if there is no risk in the final disposal of radioactive wastes, there is some risk in their transportation, and this is another doomsday possibility in the ecofanatic's arsenal; and this time it is not one that can simply be laughed away.

There are admittedly risks, for even if the probability of a mishap can be kept very small, the consequences cannot necessarily be kept small if one should happen. But here, as always, one must weigh the advantages against the disadvantages. There were no railroad disasters before railroads were buit; but that does not mean that it would be better if they had never been built. In fact, the analogy with railroads is quite a close one where environmental questions are concerned. In Europe, railroads were also fought tooth and nail on the grounds of danger, smoke and noise when they were about to appear. On studying the map of Europe's rail network, one occasionally finds strange curves in the lines that look like detours, and for which there seems to be no apparent explanation by the terrain or any other reason. But detours is exactly what they once were; the prudent city fathers of some town refused to let the fuming noisy monsters come near their town. These towns can no longer be found on the map, because these wise city fathers killed them; without access to a railroad, they eventually degenerated into unviable villages. For example, the town of Wittenberg in what is now East Germany lies on the railroad where it makes a wide arc in country that is flatter than Kansas; the town developed as a railroad junction on the arc avoiding the town which its city fathers tried to save from disaster. I have forgotten the name of that other town, and I was unable to obtain a sufficiently detailed map of East Germany that would show the name of the small remaining community, for the city fathers succeeded not only in keeping the railroad out, but also in taking their town off the map of Germany. If they were alive today, they would very likely be members of the Sierra Club or the Friends of the Earth and send checks to the Environmental Defense Fund.

While I am digressing on this precedent of self-defeating technophobia, I might as well insert another precedent: The profiteer masquerading in the cloak of the environmentalist. In many parts of what used to be the Austro-Hungarian Empire, many small communities are served by railroad stations of a peculiar kind. When the arriving visitor gets off the train, he will see the name of the community inscribed in large letters on the railroad station, but he will see no community, because the station stands alone in the fields. He will find that the community is over the hill, at a distance of half an hour's walk or sometimes more. The reason is that what today would be called the trucking business lobby (though at the time it was only horse drawn wagons) saw to it that a law was passed, more than a century ago, keeping the wagoneers in business against the rising threat of the railroads: No railroad station was to be built nearer than 2 kilometers (I am not sure of the exact figure) from the outskirts of the nearest community. Naturally they did not base their case on profits; but the good country air would be polluted by the smoke from the railroad engines. The effect can no longer be seen in the communities that have grown to envelop the railroad station; but it is usually there, for example, in the small villages of Bohemia. In the 130 years or so that have passed, it was rarely found worthwhile to lay new tracks, and for 130 years people were made to walk miles in the heat and in the dust of a road whose only purpose was to keep the profits flowing for the wagoneers. The wagoneers did not engage in transporting people, and there were no automobiles; most people did not even own horses.

As the reversionists and technophobes of yesteryear opposed the construction of railroads, so the reversionists and technophobes of today oppose the nuclear power plants. The arguments of danger and pollution are of the same kind, only the stakes have become bigger. Much of the argumentation was preposterous then, and much of it is preposterous now. Accidents with radioactive wastes are a *possibility*; increasing air pollution and shortened life spans of human beings are a stark *reality*.

BUT resources of uranium are limited, goes the old song of the doomsdaymongers. Once again, non-renewable does not mean irreplaceable. New types of reactors are already well in sight. There is, first of all, the breeder reactor, which "makes more fuel than it consumes." This statement may be misleading, because a breeder does not create matter, what it does is turn inert matter into radio-active matter which can be used for further nuclear reactions. This process goes on simultaneously with the heat produced to run a power plant; the breeder does not create matter, but it "fuelizes" it. The breeder reactor is no longer a science fiction fantasy, but it is well along the road of research and development to make it a practical reality. In 1971, the Nixon Administration announced an energy program whose main goal is the development of a liquid-metal fast-breeder reactor by 1980. Unfortunately, the project is underfunded in relation to its importance, and worse, the money has been found by cutting funds from research on other possibilities, such as the thermonuclear fusion process and the replacement of the time-honored turbogenerator altogether. With $3 billion that the breeder reactor project will cost over the next 8 years, the complaint of too little funds may seem insane. I might reply with the costs of one month of the Viet Nam war, or with the costs of air pollution (how many dollars to the human life?), but such arguments smack of demagoguery. Let me simply say that the United States is, among the highly industrialized countries, the one that spends a very small fraction of its national income on basic research; a far smaller fraction, for example, than Britain, France, West Germany or Japan. Let me also say that penny-pinching in basic research is the most foolish kind of penny pinching, for nowhere are the costs of unspent money greater; the saving is of the kind achieved when one eats the seeds instead of the harvest.

The thermonuclear fusion process is the one that fuses hydrogen nuclei into helium nuclei rather than splitting the nuclei of plutonium (see pp. 119-120). Like the breeder reactor process, this process can supply energy in virtually unlimited quantities, and although the hopes for its realization have had their ups and downs since the discovery of nuclear power, it is now generally agreed that its feasibility will be demonstrated within the present decade; in fact, the Russians claim to have achieved it already, though the claim was made only by the Soviet news agency, not in the scientific journals. A wise organizer of research will not, of course, put all his money on a single horse; but thermonuclear fusion projects are now short of funds, as is the research looking further ahead still.

There is, for example, the question whether the time-honored turbogenerator cannot be replaced by something better than mechanical power turning wire windings in a magnetic field, and whether the energy conversion chain heat — kinetic enrgy of a gas — kinetic energy of metal conductors — electric energy is the best chain of energy conversions that is feasible. The large-scale generation of electric power is based on Faraday's law, which requires electric charges to be moved through a magnetic field. These charges are now being moved in the form of free electrons in a metal conductor. But only the electrons are needed in principle; the rest of the copper only acts as a vehicle. It is also possible to shoot electrons around in beams all by themselves, in fact, such a beam is what is being manipulated in the picture tube of a television receiver. There is a promising possibility of generating power from plasma (a "gas" of electrons), again on the principle of Faraday's law, but without the use of metal conductors. The ions and electrons of a hot gas make the gas the equivalent of a conductor. A gas can, of course, be made to move by applying pressure, and this eliminates the need for thermally and mechanically stressed moving components such as the blades of a steam turbine or the rotor and its windings of an orthodox generator. Liquids at high temperatures, or a mixture of a liquid and its vapor (such as liquid potassium), can also be used as a working fluid.

The science that studies the behavior of plasma motion in electric and magnetic fields is called MHD, which is short for magneto-hydrodynamics, and its main laboratory is the universe, where electron gas is milling around in the magnetic fields of distant stars (and of close stars, such as the sun, too). This is a point to remember on hearing such wisdom as that space research is a waste of money, and that astrophysicists are people killing time by gazing through telescopes into never-never land. In any case, MHD generators face, as yet, big problems, such as containing the plasma just where one wants it, or "pinching" it (as the MHD people say) by a magnetic field. On a small laboratory scale, this can be done easily, but problems rapidly multiply with increasing dimensions and power. However, problem solving is a scientist's profession. Faraday's diary consists mostly of the blind alleys walked by Michael Faraday before he hit onto the arrangement incorporating the principle on which all major generators of electric power run today. Today's methods of organized research, backed by the digital computer, can forge ahead far faster than Faraday could in his time (1791-1867). When Faraday was asked by some society lady what use his discovery was, he answered "Madam, what use is a new-born baby?" The MHD baby is, as yet, also of little use for power generation. A baby grows on milk, and MHD grows on skills and funds. The MHD baby seems not to have been starved of its milk in the Soviet Union. In January 1972 it was announced that an MHD generator had begun operating at the Moscow Krzhizhanovsky Energy Institute; at the time of the announcement, it had logged 1,000 hours of continuous operation. It uses liquid potassium as a working fluid at $1173°K$ which enters the actual MHD generator through a jet with a velocity of 500 m/sec. The potassium flows in a closed circuit (vapor reactor, injector, MHD generator, cooler) so that no pollutants of any kind are created in the process.

Apart from the total absence of pollution, the MHD generator has another benefit. The efficiency of the conversion of heat to electric power in small and medium-sized plants is a lamentable 30 to 35%.

The rest goes through the stack and the cooling towers into the sky. The heat-electric efficiency of the MHD generator is a respectable 50 percent.

Iᴛ USED to be that a photocell (in a burglar alarm, for example) could only just indicate, by much amplification of its tiny signal, that a ray of light had hit it (or had been interrupted); the energy balance was preposterous. This is no longer the case. Semiconductors and other techniques have made it possible to gain power, not just tiny signals, from incident light; communication satellites beaming telephone conversations and television programs round the globe use this method for converting sunlight to electric power for running their electronic equipment. The vehicles moving on the surface of the moon were, in part, powered by the same process. This principle has also been used as the base for a daring proposal worked out by Dr. E. Glaser of the A.D. Little Corporation. Dr. Glaser must be a doomsday preacher's nightmare, for he has weighed the known technology and has found the following project feasible for accomplishment by the year 2000. He proposes to put up a gigantic power station as a "stationary" satellite. (At a height of about 22,300 miles above the earth, the period of one orbit is 24 hours, so that matter at that height is stationary with respect to a point on the earth's surface since it rotates at the same rate about the earth's axis.) A huge square of solar cells, 5 miles by 5 miles, would turn sunlight into electric power to be converted into the power of radio microwaves. The excess heat would be radiated away into space, whilst microwaves would be beamed to earth by a 15 mile diameter dish antenna and a receiving antenna of 6 by 6 miles would receive this energy to convert it into enough electric power to meet the demand of New York City. This is what can be done with present or shortly available technology. How does that compare with the cuts in the space budget and the gloom of the doomsday prophets?

Aden and Marjorie Meinel, astronomers at the University of Arizona, have worked out another project which captures the sun's energy on earth in a more useful way than is done now. They point out that the half million square miles that is used in the United States for agriculture yield only 1% of the country's energy needs. (Food is a source of chemical energy, which the human body turns into mechanical and other forms of energy with an efficiency that technology cannot yet come near. No man-made gadget can do comparable work at such a low temperature. Neither, for that matter, can a pedestrian's ability to accelerate be matched by any man-made vehicle of transportation). The Meinels' proposal is the solar power farm. It would use thin-film optical coating on steel pipes extending in a parallel array over large areas of desert to trap the sun's heat; this heat would be stored in molten metals and used to run a power plant in the center of the farm. The proposed power plant would produce electric power by steam-driven turbogenerators. (The steam of a power plant contains no pollutants, and it never even comes into contact with the atmosphere, since it is condensed to water after it has run through the blades of the turbine and circulates back to the water tubes of the boiler.) The Meinels' calculation shows that a solar farm of seventy-five miles square in the desert would generate no less than one million megawatts, a fantastic amount of power. Such proposals give the environmental fanatic no quarters: There is no air pollution, no waste disposal, no depletion of resources, no radioactivity, and not even "thermal pollution," for the Meinels propose to use only the solar heat that hits the desert anyway. Ah, but what will it do to the cholera germs in Bengal? Until that point is fully clarified, the courts should hit the Meinels with an injunction.

There is plenty more.The Pratt & Whittney Company has developed a fuel-cell power plant for individual homes. It runs on natural gas and converts chemical energy directly to electric power by a process that was used in the space program. It uses oxygen from the air, as do all types of present power generation except nuclear, but its only wastes are water and carbon dioxide. This non-polluting mini-plant is about as big as a small home furnace and produces 12.5 kilowatts of power, more than enough to run the kitchen range, the laundry drier and all the lights of a typical home simultaneously (the other appliances, except for air conditioners, use much less power). The energetic inefficiency of many small energy converters is offset by the absence of pollution; however, the shortage of natural gas is growing.

But there is no shortage of heat in the earth's core. Geothermal power is a source now under investigation by the Atomic Energy Commission. It is, for example, geothermal energy that powers the Old Faithful geyser in Yellowstone Park, and it will power it for ages after the present ecology fad has run its course. The Plowshare program of the AEC seeks, among other things, to create rubble cavities by deep underground atomic explosions; water can be cycled into these cavities heated by the earth's deeper layers and the resulting steam, tapped by steam lines reaching deep down into the earth's interior, can drive turbogenerators without an ounce of pollutants. The same technique of creating underground cavities can be used for tapping natural gas, oil, water, and for containing the radioactive wastes of nuclear power plants. For a continuation of the story, see p. 91 for what happened to Project Rulison.

There is more still. There is the possibility of realizing the thermonuclear fusion process "in squirts" by intermittent flashes of laser light. There is the possibility of gasification of coal and other fossils to produce clean fuel. There are the untapped funds of kinetic and potential energy of the tides. Those who truly wish to end pollution, not by first creating it and then trying to hold it back, but by eliminating it altogether, will find no lack of workable proposals; they will only find a lack of funds. They will be overwhelmed with choices to produce unlimited and pollutionless electric power.

Technology can provide the means of unlimited and pollutionless power. It can provide more and better means, not in science fiction fantasies, but in the next five to ten years. It can provide some of them now.

But there are wrenches in the works. They are wielded by the loudest voices condemning pollution, the environmental fanatics and the apoplectic apostles of apocalypse.

CONSIDER next the number one air polluter, the automobile powered by the internal combustion engine.

The American's love-hate of the automobile is a phenomenon that psychologists have not yet fully fathomed. There are, of course, a number of astonishing and unfathomed psychological phenomena that are not peculiar to any particular nation's way of life. In Britain, during the "Blitz" of 1940-42, an Englishman would take mortal offense at the suggestion that his part of the city received comparatively little damage in the bombing; had you accused his wife of being a tramp and his daughter of being a slut, his mortified indignation could not have been greater. This trait of masochistic pride is not absent in America. A few years ago, when smogs started to appear in Denver, you could hear people complain indignantly that soon Denver's mountain air would be as filthy as that of Los Angeles; but the attentive observer could not help detecting an unconscious undercurrent of pride that at last Denver was keeping up with the Joneses.

But the American's relation to the automobile is unique. If a Czech is overtaken on the road, he considers it a personal insult and by a Pavlovian reflex he steps on the accelerator to undo this offense. A German, who was meticulously polishing his Mercedes on a recent Sunday morning and was told by a passer-by that the Mercedes is a lousy car, took his gun and shot the villain who had thus besoiled his car's honor; the German jury accepted his defense of a "crime of passion," an extenuating circumstance usually reserved for husbands who shoot the lovers of their wives. Such an episode could not happen in the country that has more cars and handguns than any other. America is addicted to the automobile; but most of its citizens allege to hate it, and contemporary *bon ton* of American society requires that no opportunity be missed to spit at it.

This is not an introduction to an argument claiming that carbon monoxide is good for you. On the contrary, one of the points to be made is that the internal combustion engine has run most of its course and is about ready to be replaced by a cleaner and more efficient energy converter. Yet before this point, I cannot but add another unpopular cause to my list of unpopular causes: I would like to put in a good word for the automobile.

No single cause has made America great. There was an empty continent full of natural wealth. There were men who were unwilling to perpetuate the kind of tyranny which they had left behind. There was the melting pot which blended the skills brought from the Old World; and these skills were applied without the shackles of age-old tradition. But the automobile, surely, should not be left out in any listing of the reasons why America made such progress. Where in other countries the site of an industrial plant was usually determined by the proximity of a labor force, American industry could often make the choice on more rational grounds, such as the proximity of raw materials, because the labor force came rolling along on wheels, and many young American cities developed from what was once a trailer park. The long story of productivity in American agriculture began with the tractor, which replaced the horses that are to this day used in less advanced countries. The millions of families that moved to more pleasant surroundings in the suburbs could do so because of the automobile, which enabled the breadwinner to commute to the city; no such choice was open to the inhabitants of the overcrowded cities in countries where only the very rich could, until recently, afford a car. No school buses are needed in these cities; the children walk to school in these cities, and they walk to school for miles in the country. What shocked European readers in Steinbeck's *Grapes of Wrath* was not the poverty of a family that lost its farm, for they were well acquainted with evictions; what shocked them was that such a family still had a truck with which to move across a continent. Many of those who clamor for the quality of life and a natural environment would never have known much quality of life, and would never have seen much natural environment, without the automobile. It would be easy enough to list a thousand other examples of how the automobile helped make America what it is. Surely the machine that made all this possible does not deserve to be spat on now that the usefulness of its engine is drawing to a close. Henry Ford, with all his faults, was still the man whose vision put a nation on wheels, and any other nation would have worshiped him as one of its greatest sons; but in America, Bat Masterson and Joe Dillinger are found much more interesting, and Henry Ford is insulted by having a Roman I added to his name as if he needed identification like a mere monarch of some decadent dynasty. Even the interstate network and the freeways of the cities are regarded as a necessary evil in the manner of a garbage dump or sewage pipes. Yet few Americans have seen the freeways except through their windshields. Among man-made things that serve a useful purpose, the multiple interchanges in Los Angeles or San Francisco have an unusual beauty in the eyes of those who stop to behold them. But there are few beholders of the traffic paths supported by slender columns, majestically sweeping through space and intertwining like the themes of a Bachian fugue.

However, let us cast aside sentimental and aesthetic considerations, and let us take a look at the sheer technological facts. The internal combustion engine, now all but 100 years old, has a lamentably low energetic efficiency, and when run on gas or oil, the presently used fuels, it produces both poisonous gases and particulate pollutants. The internal combustion engine is America's number one air polluter. It is estimated that 70% of the pollutants in the atmosphere above urban and industrial areas found their way into the air through automobile exhausts, and though methods of measuring air pollution are not yet very accurate, the estimate cannot be radically in error, for more reliable statistics point in the same direction. The consumption of crude petroleum, most of which is used to produce gasolene, amounts to almost 40% of the total consumption of energy resources, and transportation amounts to about one quarter of the consumption of energy (exceeding, individually, the generation of electric power, the other needs of industry, and the energy consumed in households and commercial enterprises). Cars, trucks, buses and motorcycles amount to about 95% of the total horse power of all prime movers.

Since the automobile in its present form is the number one air polluter, it is logical that it should get number one priority in the stop-gap measures that are now on the books, and that will soon be enforced. However, for a permanent solution, the number one candidate is the pollutionless generation of electric power, which is the ultimate source of virtually all pollution control, and which will eventually charge the power sources of the electric car. The electric car is now the only substitute in sight for replacing the heat-engine driven car, and what use will that be if the pollution comes out of the stacks of the power plants instead of the car exhausts? True, it would be of *some* use, since the total amount of pollution would be smaller, and the source of the pollution could be placed where fewer people object to it, but in the long run, this only amounts to borrowing from Peter to pay Paul.

As in the case of power stations, there are two ways of controlling pollution: One is to create pollutants and then try to get rid of them, the other is not to create pollutants in the first place. The first method is the one now being adopted by equiping cars with both internal combustion engines and anti-emission devices. The second method, as things stand now, is to use pollutionless fuels or to replace the internal combustion engine by a battery-driven electric motor. There is, of course, also the third method of reducing the number of cars by rational use of mass transportation, or by irrational use of de-development, but I leave these points for later.

The situation is, however, not the same as with power plants. The technology for the pollutionless generation of electric power is ready here and now, and the methods of pollution control in the stack are not very highly effective. For automobiles, the converse is true: The technology of producing a pollutionless car is not ready and cannot be expected before the end of the decade; but the methods of trapping the pollutants of a gasolene-powered engine before they are emitted through the exhaust are highly effective, though not perfect.

In saying that a pollutionless car is not ready, I mean a pollutionless car that is able to compete with the presently used cars because consumers will find it equally or more attractive, not because they are forced into it by prohibiting the internal combustion engine. An electric car representing essentially a large amount of short-lived batteries on wheels, with a range of 50 miles and very poor acceleration, is ready now.

Fortunately, there are strong indications to suggest that the half-way measure of trapping pollutants after they are created (rather than eliminating them altogether) works very effectively in the case of automobiles. The reasons for this are mainly technical, but they are also administrative. Technically, the pollution control devices now being prepared for the 1975 car models are so effective that the few drops spilled in filling the gas tank of a car are comparable to the pollution that manages to penetrate through the emission control devices in many miles of driving. The emission standards for automobiles to be enforced by 1975 are so strict that there is some doubt whether the auto industry will be able to comply with them by 1975. A battle to prolong the deadline may yet shape up between the auto industry and those who demand excessive speed in technological development only when it suits them. However, it may well be that the auto industry will be ready with the corresponding devices by 1975. Such a development will hardly be brought about by anybody's personal vendetta against General Motors; if it does come about, it will come from a company bent on increasing its profits by superior technology. It now seems probable that the Japanese company Toyo Kogyo, which is marketing the Mazda cars with the rotary engine, is such a company. In a little over a year since the cars with this engine have been marketed, they have shot to fourth place in California among the sales of imported cars. According to estimates of experts in the car industry (who are not, of course, infallible), 75 to 95% of all engines produced in the United States in 1980 will be rotaries.

The rotary or Wankel engine is still an internal combustion engine, but its explosion does not drive a piston and it therefore needs no connecting rod or crankshaft to convert the linear motion of a piston into the rotation of the drive shaft; the explosion rotates a rotor whose tips are touching the walls of the combustion chamber, and this rotational motion is transmitted to the drive shaft. Geometrically, the underlying principle might be formulated by saying that the circle is not the only figure that has a constant width when rolled between two parallel lines (see figure on p. 138), and a circle is not the only figure inside which something can be rolled whilst constantly touching the circumference by one of its tips. The first rotary engine based on this abstract principle was built by Dr. Felix

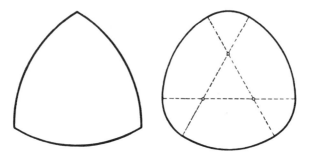

Two examples of geometrical figures (other than the circle) that can be rolled between two parallel lines at a constant distance from each other. Both figures are made up from circular arcs. The one on the left has its arcs centered at the apices of an equilateral triangle, the other uses six arcs centered at the three points shown.

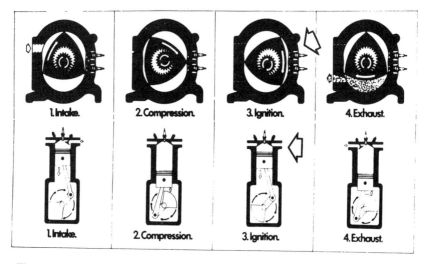

The rotary and the reciprocating engines. Note the shape of the compression space on the third stroke. Its surface to volume ratio is much larger for the rotary engine than for the conventional engine. This results in lower peak temperatures for the rotary engine, and hence in less nitrogen oxides.

Wankel of the German company NSU, which has since become a subsidiary of Volkswagen. The first operating model was built in 1957, but it took eleven more years of development, most of it done by Toyo Kogyo, to produce an engine that could compete with the reciprocating engine after the latter had been through a century of constant development, refinement and ramification. The result is an engine which has 40% fewer parts, weighs from a third to half as much, is half the size, makes much less noise, and is much cheaper to build — at the beginning of its career.

However, I am not a Mazda salesman; the point here is that the rotary engine creates less pollutants in its operation, and it enables them to be suppressed more easily. According to some experts, the rotary engine, without any emission controls and only at its present beginning of development, is cleaner than the conventional engines were in the early sixties. This is, in part, due to the lower peak temperatures attained in the combustion chamber, which has a greater metal surface to volume ratio to dissipate the heat (see lower figure on opposite page, ignition stroke). The peak temperatures of the orthodox combustion engine are high, and they are the reason for the generation of nitrogen oxides, which are the most difficult pollutants to eliminate in the operation of an automobile. The generation of hydrocarbons is also said to be smaller (for reasons unknown to me), whilst the generation of carbon monoxide is about the same for both types of engine. Moreover, the rotary engine makes it much easier to control the emission of pollutants after they have been produced in the combustion chamber. Part of the emission control is based on the principle of burning the pollutants exiting from the combustion chamber in an afterburner; a simple realization of this idea is the thermal reactor, which mixes fresh air with the hot exhaust gases to ignite them. This simple device works efficiently with a rotary engine because its exhaust temperatures are higher. The reason is much the same as why its peak combustion temperatures are lower: There is more metal to dissipate the heat in the combustion chamber, but less metal in the exhaust, since the rotary engine substitutes a simple hole for the exhaust ports and valves of an orthodox engine. The difference is particularly conspicuous during warm up, when an engine works very inefficiently; in fact, one can regard a choke as a device for radically reducing the efficiency of an engine, since it will enrich the mixture produced in the carburetor so as to produce great amounts of heat. The exhaust ports and valves of an orthodox engine take a long time to warm up, and the resulting inefficiency of the thermal reactor is such that 30 seconds warm-up will undo all the emission control of an hour's driving. This is not so with the rotary engine, whose exhaust gases go through a mere hole into the thermal reactor. This reactor, incidentally, can easily be fitted into the engine compartment of a car with a rotary engine, which is only half as big as an orthodox one, whereas there is no space left to mount it in the present type of engine compartment: Detroit's engineers are still forced to cram their designs into whatever the stylists have concocted. This is something like designing the casing and jacket of a book and then asking an author to fill the pages with text; the logic is the same, but the technical difficulties are much greater for the automobile engineer.

The comparative (and only comparative) ease with which the polluting emissions of a rotary engine can be controlled has given the American auto industry a bigger shock than all the clamor of the environmentalists (who admittedly did a good thing in starting the clamor). Whilst the auto lobbies were busy in Washington explaining the impossibility of meeting the required standards by 1975, the Toyo Kogyo company coolly informed the Environmental Protection Agency in the spring of 1972 that preliminary tests of their rotary engines indicated that they should be able to conform to the standards set by Congress for the 1975 models. An army of Ralph Naders could hardly have shocked the auto industry more; superior technology once again proved stronger than the hysterical "I don't care how you do it" demands. General Motors has already shelled out the first $15 million of a $50 million licensing deal to become a licencee of the Wankel engine, and Ford, Chrysler, and the others will doubtlessly have to get in on the rotary engine, too. Auto companies have a way of fearing loss of a market more than the protests of the environmentalists, and whilst the crusaders are writing articles on the profits in pollution, the profit motive seems to have made a corporation develop a piece of superior technology that promises to impose a significant curb on pollution.

These curbs will not, of course, come free. The cost of emission control devices will be about $250 per car, not counting the maintenance of the equipment. However, people may feel, with good reason, that this is a bargain for the benefit of clean air; the cost is also justly borne by the potential polluter, and it is even possible that the owner of the car may get a small part of his money back in lower gas costs: Much of pollution control is based on the principle of getting more power out of the gas in the combustion chamber and not let it escape through the exhaust, so that some (but not all) emission control might result in better gas mileage. However, this remark concerns only the efficiency of energy conversion, and only in part. The actual power available from the gasolene engine is steadily being reduced by pollution control devices, and in some cases it may reach the point where the smaller power of engines not running on gasolene may become competitive.

The standards for emission control set for the 1975 models are extraordinarily strict, and there now seems a good chance that the required technology will be ready in time. But apart from the technical considerations, these standards also have a very good chance of proving effective from the administrative point of view. With the exception of automobile emission standards, the legislation intended to curb air pollution leaves enforcement in the hands of the states, who at present do not have the means to measure air pollution accurately, let alone prevent it. The most conspicuous effect that the 1971 Environmental Protection Act appears to have had so far is the requirement to issue statements on the impact on the environment, and these statements, or their insufficiency, have been used by the Sierra Club, the Friends of the Earth, and other pollution-minded organizations to thwart the construction of nuclear power plants in particular, and the growth of technology in general, so that in the long run the effect of these friends of the earth is to create more pollution by blindly invoking the legislation designed to curb it. However, in the case of automobile emissions, enforcement is left to the federal government, and it is comparatively easy to enforce at the source of sources, that is, directly in the auto industry. This is not to suggest that the federal government is necessarily more competent than state governments; basically, the difference is that pollution is more easily measured at the end of a car exhaust than in a stack (where, at present, measurement is difficult or impossible), and it is more easily curbed in a car engine than in the stacks of an industrial plant. It follows that law enforcement is easier also.

In the face of these encouraging facts on automobile emission control, the technophobes and de-developers present us with a profound argument: Even if the 1975 models have effective pollution control devices, there will still be many polluting older models on the road in 1985. They would presumably have opposed inoculation against polio on the grounds that it did no good for the people who had already contracted the disease. However, there is no need for such hypothetical arguments, because the statistics reject this argument, not in 1985, but now, in 1972, two years before the 1975 models have reached the showrooms. It is true that at present about 84% of the automobile-generated air pollution comes from the older cars not equiped with the anti-pollution devices introduced by the auto industry in the past few years. Yet these devices, such as the crank case ventilation system introduced in 1963 and the gasolene vapor burning system introduced in 1971, which go only part of the way in meeting the standards set for the 1975 models, are already more than compensating for the increased number of cars on the road: *The total automobile-generated air pollution in the United States is already decreasing from its peak reached in the middle sixties.* The National Air Pollution Control Commission, which is hardly a mouthpiece of the ecocult-begotten "more profits through more pollution" Demons of Detroit, estimates that by the end of this decade hydrocarbon and carbon monoxide emissions will, inspite of the increasing number of automobiles, be back to their pre-World War II levels. Even now, they are low compared to the mid-1960's. Such estimates are based not only on the rising number of cars, but also on the rising efficiency of technological devices to combat their emission, as well as on the already measured data on this point. But they are dutifully ignored by the computerized soothsayers whose doomsday machines run on Hardin's Law "Population times prosperity equals pollution."

But if the situation should warrant it, even problems created by older cars can at least partially be tackled. It is probable that poor people who are now being told by the business executives in the Sierra Club that the trouble with the world is too much prosperity, would not take kindly to a law forcing them to buy $500 worth of anti-pollution devices for their model 1957 Chevvies, and this is not what I am proposing. There are, however, great reserves in what can be done to reduce the emission of pollutants without sophisticated contraptions. A study by the University of Michigan showed that an average of 55% reduction in pollution levels can be achieved by a pure and simple tune-up. A dirty air cleaner, for example, can lead to a drastic increase in carbon monoxide emissions by causing an unnecessarily rich mixture, and a little gasolene to wash it out will do more for carbon monoxide suppression than the various devices that the scientists have yet come up with.

Another important reserve among these stop-gap measures, which is not limited to old cars, is a very simple expedient that seems to have received little attention. An automobile's emission increases

AUTOMOTIVE HYDROCARBON EMISSIONS
UNITED STATES

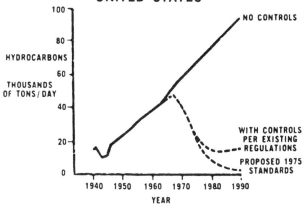

AUTOMOTIVE CARBON MONOXIDE EMISSIONS
UNITED STATES

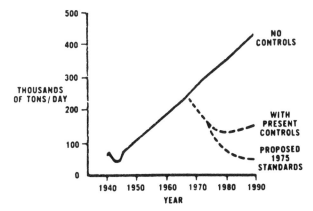

Data published by the National Air Pollution Control Commission in May 1972. In spite of the increasing number of cars, pollution from automobiles is at a lower level than a decade ago. By 1980, pollution levels are expected to recede to approximately pre-World War II levels.

drastically when it accelerates, and the greatest acceleration of which
a car is capable occurs at zero velocity, that is, when it starts from
rest. Not only is the rate of pollution maximum under those conditions, but the pollutants also achieve a maximum concentration in
the surrounding air, since the car is standing or moving at a very low
velocity. The most common instance when this happens is, of course,
when a group of cars starts after a traffic light has changed from red
to green, and the possibility of synchronizing a city's traffic lights so
as to assure the maximum flow of traffic have rarely been considered
by those who blame all automobile pollution on technology in
general and the Demons of Detroit in particular. Computer controlled traffic lights would work wonders in reducing air pollution,
but even the oldfashioned methods of producing a "green wave"
could often reduce automobile emissions by a significant amount.
Boulder, Colorado, for example, is stricken with an unusual abundance of environmental groups demanding less population, less technology, less growth, less pollution, less noise, less auto traffic, and
more recruits, means and facilities for their causes. The first resource that seems in danger of being totally depleted is the English
alphabet, for each such group has chosen a pronouncable acronym
for itself, and one group (though, in fairness, it is not an environmental one) has chosen the acronym BURP. The automobile and its
emissions are a prime target of the various PUREs, PLANs and
other alphabet depleters, and one rousing appeal published in the
local press ended with the indignant outcry "Stop that car!" The
1971 elections were largely fought on the environmental issue and
resulted in a resounding vioctory of the environmentalists, who now
overwhelmingly populate the city council. Nevertheless, on driving
through the city, one is perplexed by the thought that mere randomness in switching the traffic lights could result in such an effective
way of stopping the traffic at almost every intersection.

However, the environmentalists do have a point, as they have one
in many other issues, in pointing out that any type of pollution
control after pollutants have been created in the first place must
sooner or later become ineffective when the number of cars becomes
sufficiently large. There is the experience made in California, where
state legislation some years ago required pollution control devices
which cut the emission in half, but by the time the legislation was
finally passed, the number of cars had about doubled, so that
California only just managed to hold its own, but made no inroads
on air pollution. Although the 1975 standards are exceedingly strict,

so that the same thing will not happen within five years after the standards are complied with, they are not a solution that will get at the root of the problem. Present projections of pollutants emitted by automobiles indicate that the new devices will more than compensate for the increasing number of cars until about 1990, so that the total pollution will steadily decrease until it reaches pre-World War II levels and falls below them; however, if nothing else is done, the rising number of cars will eventually make the curve flatten out, and some time after 1990 it will start rising again. Obviously, then, the new emission control devices are not a permanent solution. Disregarding for the moment the de-developers' recipe of curtailing the number of cars, this leaves the totally pollutionless car as the only alternative.

At present, there are only two roads in sight to reach this alternative, though the future may hold some surprises. One road is to keep the present combustion engine, either in its orthodox or rotary form, and use fuels that create no pollutants. One such possibility is liquid hydrogen, which creates no pollution; its only waste is water vapor, and the generation of nitrogen oxides can be kept below a measurable level. Hydrogen is in virtually unlimited supply, since it is made by electrolysis from water, or sea water if necessary. The price of liquid hydrogen is competitive with that of gasolene, it can be transported almost as safely, and it contains more energy per unit weight than any other fuel now known. The main problems associated with its use seem to be those connected with its storage, handling and distribution. The range of experimental models is also small: The supply of one hydrogen cylinder lasts for only about 150 miles. I have not been able to trace a large research program devoted to this possibility; only a small group of students at UCLA seems to be working on it. There is little doubt that the skills are available; if nowhere else, then perhaps in some of the supermarket checkouts now manned by aerospace engineers who were fired when the aerospace industry was starved of projects and left to go into decline. The environmental fanatics are not calling for them; they are working on decimating what is left of the aerospace industry.

Some funds have been given to research on gas turbine engines. The R. Lear Company in Reno, Nevada, has built a bus driven by a steam turbine with kerosene as a fuel. Kerosene is a low pollution fuel, and the small external combustion engines used in automobiles do not generate nitrogen oxides. However, though pollution is low, it is not totally absent, and there are formidable problems associated with reducing the size of the auxiliary equipment (the turbine is quite small, but the condenser and pumps take up much space). Perhaps surprisingly, one of the main problems is the absence of a gas with better properties than steam at high temperatures and pressures.

Other possibilities, such as an internal combustion engine running on methane and driving a generator to power an electric car, are also under investigation, but this does not appear very hopeful in finding a permanent solution.

The other road, that of replacing the internal combustion engine altogether, has received more attention, and it has mostly been devoted to the production of an electric car. The main thrust of the research has been directed toward finding a suitable battery to power such a car. This research is conducted at the Argonne National Laboratory and at a number of universities and smaller companies. The auto industry is not very communicative on its research, and only occasional items in the press indicate some research on the battery powered electric car.

There is at present no car that can effectively compete with the car driven by the internal combustion engine. After more than half a century of refining the car powered by a heat engine, it is not surprising to encounter difficulties in making an entirely new system competitive. The rotary engine is still an internal combustion engine, whereas the electric car represents an entirely different system. Fifty years ago, the present electric cars would have been hailed as a miracle of technology, but who can blame contemporary consumers for rejecting a product that is inferior in almost every respect except pollution?

The main difficulty encountered in the development of the battery powered electric car is the battery, whose present energy density (capacity of storing energy per unit volume) is so small that either the range of the car is limited to some 50 miles before recharging (or exchanging) the battery, or the car has to carry so many batteries that it becomes little more than a battery on wheels.

Unfortunately, this is not the only difficulty. Polls taken in 1970 indicate that 50 million Americans would be interested in buying a short-range, limited-speed electric car if one were available under $2,000. This represents an increase of about 14 million over a similar poll taken 3 years earlier. Since most cars are driven to and from work in or near a city, a 50 mile range and a top speed of almost 60 mph seems an eminently reasonable proposition in exchange for cleaner air. However, range and speed are not the only things that a driver has to consider; there is also acceleration and operating costs, for example, and these are very unfavorable in contemporary electric cars. Acceleration from rest to 50 mph takes about 40 seconds, and longer still from 50 mph to the top speed of less than 60 mph. This may be sufficient for congested city traffic, but it is not enough to get out of a jam quickly, and it is not enough to attract the driver who has been used to a combustion engine. The various models of such cars mostly use the lead-acid type battery presently used for powering the starter of an orthodox car engine. Such batteries are relatively inexpensive when replacement is needed only once every two years, but the cost becomes prohibitive if the life of the battery is shortened to a few months, corresponding to an operating life measured in cycles of full discharge and recharge of the battery. Improvement of the operating life of present lead-acid or other types of batteries would solve the main problem confronting the limited-range limited-speed electric car for use in city traffic. The remaining problems are relatively minor and would presumably be solved by development rather than research — problems such as designing a compact and reliable transmission suitable for mass production at low cost. Though the use of such a car would be strictly limited, it is possible that it might provide a partial solution to transportation within cities.

But such a car could not replace the present heat engine altogether. A high performance electric car capable of competing with the performance of contemporary automobile engines would need a battery with as yet unattained properties. Design goals for battery programs funded by the federal government include, among others, the following specifications:* The energy density is to be 220 watt-hours per kilogram of weight, and the power density required to match the present acceleration of the orthodox car engine is to be 220 watts per kilogram. The life time of the battery should be a minimum of 5 years or 1000 cycles, corresponding to some 60,000 miles of operation under adverse conditions. The price goal is $2.20 per kilogram, or $10 per kilowatthour.

Research to produce such high energy-density and high power-density batteries at a low price is now being conducted at the Argonne National Laboratory, at several universities and in private

---

* These figures are based on a report by J.T. Salihi, *Two for the Road*, IEEE Spectrum, July 1972, pp. 43-47. Dr. Salihi is with the Advanced Automotive Power Systems Division of the Environmental Protection Agency.

industry, but long range research of this type where the pay-off does not follow closely on the heels of the investment needs large funds, which are not forthcoming in the quantities corresponding to the importance of the problem and the likelihood of its solution.

For it is indeed likely that such batteries will be developed. The zinc-chloride, sodium-sulfur and lithium sulfur batteries, now under investigation, appear to be highly promising, as do some other batteries; in fact, some of these batteries have already achieved the required energy and power densities, but only at very high temperatures, and some progress has already been made in attaining these properties at low temperatures. There is also the alternative of tackling the problems arising from high temperatures in practical applications. It is, of course, not possible to make a forecast of the date when a breakthrough will be made. But breakthroughs are usually achieved when the problem has been reduced to the "trade off" state — when some of the required properties can be achieved at the expense of others, or when all properties can be achieved, but not at the same time. The as yet unattained "superbattery" needed for the electric car is now in that state or very close to it, and if the above criterion is any guide, a breakthrough cannot be very long in coming if research is conducted intensively on a wide front.

B UT why not curb the number of cars instead of waging a constant battle against the pollution growing with every additional car on the road? Here, as so often, the environmentalists have a point; the idea of millions of people driving to work, each encased in a voluminous box of steel and polluting the air all the way, is indeed ludicrous. But here again the basic criterion will serve to separate the reasonable from the fanatics: Should the number of cars be curbed by letting more advanced technology provide more attractive forms of mass transportation, or should transportation de-develop back to low efficiencies and perhaps to the bicycle and the horse and cart? Should people be regimented into mass transportation by coercive laws and prohibitions, or should a man be given a choice which does not deprive him of the right to go where he likes when he likes?

Here again, more technology, and not less, can provide the answer. As one of many examples, take the housewife who goes shopping. In countries where the automobile has not yet dominated transportation, she takes a bus and carries her purchases in a basket or bag, often a long way from the nearest bus stop; she has to go shopping almost every day, for she cannot carry the five or six bags of groceries that the American housewife takes home in her car from the supermarket once a week. To take a taxi every day is too expensive, and in any case, it makes no difference whether the roads are clogged by private cars or taxis. Buses with fixed routes and schedules do not solve much; American cities have found them a losing proposition financially, and zero relief from traffic congestion. But there is a compromise between the bus and the taxi: The minibus that runs for several persons along the route and at the time determined (more or less) by the passengers. What makes such a proposal realistic is the digital computer, which can work out the schedules and routes from the incoming demands far more efficiently than a human dispatcher, and it does not draw as large a salary paid for by the fare. This system is now in its infancy, and it is too early to say whether it will survive and significantly reduce traffic congestion; but surely the use of a digital computer is more realistic and hopeful than the bicycle.

Superior technology can also solve the problem of mass transportation for commuters. Even contemporary railroad technology could be, by any criterion, a better way to transport a thousand people than to seat them in one thousand cars to increase the jam on the freeway. But if railroads are forced by law to run unprofitable trains, they will end up exactly where they have ended: in bankruptcy, or with a service used by the passengers not because they find it more attractive, but because they find it less horrible. The trains of the Long Island Railroad in New York carry commuters wearing buttons with the inscription "I hate the Long Island Railroad." Is that the quality of life the de-developers have in mind?

But if millions of motorists prefer the dangers and the snail's pace of a jammed freeway to other forms of transportation, it is not the fault of technology. If any proof of such a self-evident statement is required, then it has been supplied by the Lindenwold Line now in operation near Camden, New Jersey. Although it is only 14.5 miles long, and although it uses none of the technology that has been proposed for future mass transit systems, it is being intensively studied not only by transportation experts from all over the United States, but also from Mexico, Europe and Russia, who come to inspect the unbelievable miracle: The railroad has taken 40% of commuter automobile traffic off the road; it has reduced the rush hour traffic across the Ben Franklin Bridge by 1,900 vehicles, and the traffic that used to crawl over the bridge at snail's pace is now moving freely. How many millions in additional taxes must be levied to pay for this miracle? Not a cent; the Delaware River Port Authority, which runs the line, is breaking even on the 30 to 60 cent fares paid gladly by the passengers, and it is even running up a small profit.

This miracle is no miracle. It would have been a miracle if it had been achieved by legislation, prohibition, ordinances, and regulations. But the planners of this little transit system used an unheard of new gimmick to lure the commuters out of their cars: They made the railroad more attractive and less expensive. They used available technology to make the trains fast, frequent and comfortable; and they minimized operating costs by automating the operation of the railroad to the fullest possible extent.

And with such devious tricks they succeeded. A full 40% of the passengers are commuters who used to drive to Philadelphia, crowding not only the road into the city, but also its parking spaces; another 13% are people who did not commute to Philadelphia before, because they could not face the predicament of the commuter. The electric cars of the trains accelerate from rest to 50 mph in 20 seconds. The cruising speed is 75 mph. Heavy, continuous-welded rails provide a smooth ride with a minimum of outside noise. The inside of the cars is insulated from noise and air conditioned. The trains run in 10 minute intervals, and in 5 minute intervals during the rush hour. Each train carries only one employee, an attendant who opens and closes the doors and pushes a button to start the train after each stop. All other operations, including acceleration, regulating cruising speed, braking, and bringing the train to a stop, are performed electronically and automatically. The passengers buy their tickets from machines and pass through automated turnstiles. The system has 145 passengers for each employee, including guards and janitors, and thus breaks even on the 30 to 60 cent fares, and on the 25 cent parking fee (dropped in some places after 10 a.m. to encourage off-peak users of the trains). This is testimony to what superior technology can do for pollution abatement. There is also testimony what legislation can sometimes do against it: The empty trucks that run between the cities of the continent as a result of ICC rules and regulations.*

---

* For more details on the Lindenwold Line, see C.G. Burck, *The Little Railroad That Could*, Fortune, July 1971, pp. 74-77. The same issue also contains an article on the wastes in interstate freight transportation, *Transportation's Troubled Abundance*.

If a 14.5 mile long railroad can do such wonders in reducing automobile traffic by using what is by now orthodox technology, how much more can be done by the technology that is now on the horizon?

Long-distance tube trains can run through tunnels in the earth at speeds approaching those of airplanes. These tunnels need not be bored by the slow and cumbersome methods of yesterday; the Los Alamos Scientific Laboratory has produced an electrically or nuclearly heated projectile that will melt its way through the hardest rock, and Westinghouse Electric is developing an electron gun that slices through rockface not like, but faster than, a knife slices through butter. Private industry, under contract from the Department of Transportation, is experimenting with rubber-tired, computer controlled, self-service cars holding up to 15 passengers and running along automated guideways. But the United States, perhaps partly owing to the influence of the technophobes, de-developers and doomsday preachers, is no longer in the lead of developing mass transportation systems; it is lagging more and more behind Europe and Japan. Britain developed the hovercraft, whose principle is now being applied to air cushion trains without wheels; Britain also developed the "linear induction motor," in principle an electric motor with the rotor spread out along the rail of a high-speed train, and the stator (which produces an alternating magnetic field) replaced by the train itself. These principles have been combined in France's "Aerotrain" and Britain's "Hovertrain." But already these principles are being challenged by new designs now being tested in Germany and Japan; the train is kept afloat above the guiding track by electromagnetic forces. The US contribution to all of these revolutionary methods of mass transportation consists of small programs, all of which are late starters; the old story of too little, too late. However that may be, the Lindenwold Line now in operation, and the aerotrains, hovertrains and electromagnetic trains now on the test tracks, demonstrate how superior technology can solve the problems of mass transportation.

What moron will want to replace these possibilities with the bicycle?

5

The
Computerized Soothsayers

*You can't commit suicide! It's against Roman
Law. The penalty is death.*
From the film "A funny thing happened to me
on the way to the Forum."

It is my opinion that the ecocult and doomsday philosophy have
produced no result more pathetic than *The Limits to Growth* and
similar computer programs that obediently produce what has been
put into them: doomsday. It does not take much demography to see
through Dr. Ehrlich's jests, and no one who is even a little interested
in science will seriously believe that we will ever run out of all energy
resources. But it is another matter to browbeat people who have
never heard of systems theory or stability criteria with a stack of
ominously looking computer print-outs, and to present the public
with pretentious, half-baked results conforming to the doomsday
philosophy as if those results were meaningful.

The assumptions on which these programs are based are false or
arbitrary; if the assumptions are accepted *pro suppositione*, the
results are trivial; and contrary to the authors' implications, the
unstable model they have produced cannot be stabilized.

This much I conclude from the flow charts, print-outs and what
little details of the programs the authors of *The Limits to Growth**
included in their book; some of the errors also appear, though less
blatantly, in the original *World Dynamics*,† from which *The Limits
to Growth* are derived, and which gives full details of the computation. As for the text accompanying the print-outs in *The Limits
to Growth*, it appears to me that the hollow alibïs ("These graphs

---

* D. H. Meadows, D. L. Meadows, J. Randers, W. W. Behrens, *The Limits to
Growth*, Universe Books, New York, 1972.

† J.W. Forrester, *World Dynamics*, Wright-Allen Press, Cambridge, Mass., 1971.

are not exact predictions. . . The model is. . . imperfect, oversimplified and unfinished. . .") are drowned out by alarmist calls to save the world from imminent disaster by artificially arresting economic and technical growth; the entire book is a jungle of intertwined truths and fictions.

But before trying to disentangle these truths and fictions, I feel it important to repeat a point made in connection with other authors. I consider *The Limits to Growth* embarrassingly lacking in integrity, but I hold this opinion of the work, not its authors. I have no doubt that the authors of both *The Limits to Growth* and *World Dynamics* did not act against their better consciences, and that they sincerely believe it their duty to warn the world against a disaster of whose imminent threat they have fully convinced themselves. I have no reason to believe otherwise. But as before, I am not a psychologist interested in how the authors got trapped into a mistaken belief in spite of their good intentions; I am exclusively concerned with their book and computer programs, not with the good intentions that may have motivated them.

To disentangle the truths and fictions of *The Limits to Growth*, we have to go back to some basics.

It is a scientist's job to search for truth, more particularly, for general truths. It is a general, and therefore important, truth that properties acquired since birth cannot be inherited; it is a particular, and therefore less important, truth that Jewish boys are still born with their foreskins in spite of five thousand years of circumcision.

The criterion for truth in all inductive sciences (which in practice means all sciences except mathematics) is agreement with experience: A natural law, for example, is accepted as true if it explains all pertinent phenomena and is contradicted by none. In their search for truth, the inductive sciences take it for granted that nature is consistent. It is accepted that water attains its greatest density at 4° C, because all experiments ever made have confirmed it, and none have contradicted it. If someone says that there is no proof that this is so until all the water in the universe has been measured, he has a point, but a point that will probably only interest philosophers; scientists have a fundamental belief in the consistency of nature.

It is, however, perfectly permissible to make assumptions, i.e., to postulate a state of affairs without experimental evidence. In the inductive sciences, this may be done for a variety of reasons. One such reason is what might be called "justification by succes." If the assumption leads to conclusions that agree with observation, then the assumption may be justified by such an indirect demonstration, although it remains a mere hypothesis until it is reasonably certain that *only* this assumption explains the experimental evidence. For example, Max Planck had no direct experimental evidence of any kind to justify his hypothesis that energy can be increased or decreased only in small, discrete quantum jumps rather than continuously; but such a hypothesis led to perfect agreement with observation in the case of radiation by a black body. Since then, this assumption has proved very fruitful in explaining, and even predicting, thousands of other observations, and it has not once been contradicted; until it is, it is accepted as true.

The "assumption justified by success" is not the only kind of acceptable assumption in the inductive sciences. There are many other reasons why assumptions are made. There is the assumption by self-evidence, by irrelevance, by default, and many others (these are not accepted terms, I have used them here in the hope of clarifying things). The assumption by self-evidence is one that is used to save time; a hypothetical opponent would concede it without requiring proof. For example, if a scientist calculates certain effects in meteor showers and says "assuming that gravitational interaction has no effect," he means "Don't make me prove that the gravitational attraction between two meteors is negligible compared to the earth's gravitation and other forces; this is self-evident, and if you do not agree, check it out for yourself."

This type of assumption, which I have here called assumption by self-evidence, abounds in *The Limits to Growth*. There is nothing wrong with the *type* of assumption, what is wrong are the assumptions themselves, for they are neither self-evident nor valid. The authors spend a good deal of time defending themselves from potential attackers on issues on which no reasonable oppoenent will ever attack them. On the other hand, they offer no explanation as to why more people must mean more pollution; they seem to regard this as self-evident, and they use pollution as one of their many weapons of multiple overkill. Yet the assumption is patently false; it is not only false by logical analysis of what can reasonably be expected in the future, it is also false by contradiction with observation. The population of the United States has been increasing for the last 10 years, whilst air pollution first increased, and in the last five years it has been decreasing; pollution levels are now lower than they were a decade ago (see figures on p. 143). Since the model attempts to simulate worldwide conditions, a hundred other contradictions could be given, but the example of the United States is sufficient to make the assumption unacceptable (see also Chapter 4). Had the authors assumed a dependence of the type "The more people, the more plague," it would have been equally unacceptable, yet the time span during which such a correlation was valid was longer than that on which the authors base their pseudo-correlation between population and pollution. As an assumption by self-evidence, the assumption is unacceptable; but the authors would have done better to leave it at that. Their attempts to prop it up (in the sense of an assumption justified by success) by quoting such data as the carbon dioxide concentration measured in Hawaii is a possibly unintended, but unacceptable hoax to which I will return later. The false assumption is partially withdrawn in one of the runs, where the authors admit that nuclear power might slow the rate of growth of pollution; but there are several runs of this type which merely exhibit the model's undisputed capability of leading to doom under all conditions: If pollution does not get us, we will all be killed by starvation via the route of lengthened life span, population increase and food shortage. If one false assumption will not lead to doom, another will.

The "self-evident" assumption that mineral and other resources must eventually be used up is equally arbitrary. We are presented with a table of presently known supplies and asked to swallow the postulate that resources will run out in 250 years (or double that time in a run to suicide by other means). We are told quite a bit about relations between resource depletion and GNP, S-shaped curves and many other hypotheses, but the basic question, whether resources will indeed ever run out is avoided, presumably as self-evident. The authors do not ask what a table of "presently" known resources looked like 100 years ago, nor do they counter the obvious objection that non-renewable does not mean irreplaceable; it is self-evident that a box of candies is eventually eaten up, and so are resources.

To return to assumptions, there is another type of assumption, which I have called assumption by irrelevance. If I wish to prove that a suction pump cannot raise water to a height of 100 feet, I am justified in making the patently false assumption that the pump is 100% efficient and creates a 100% vacuum; under these assumptions the pump will not pump the water even to 60 feet. If the assumption is withdrawn, a much more complicated calculation will result in an even smaller height, and this type of assumption therefore again amounts to a time-saving device by not going into irrelevancies. This type of assumption, in itself blameless, is used in *The Limits to Growth* abundantly. It is used on every run that demonstrates the reliability of committing suicide along all roads. Using the assumption by irrelevance in the form of doubling resources or slowing the rate of pollution or increasing the per capita food production in essence amounts to saying "Let him have more clean air, we will starve him to death anyway. He doesn't like it? So let him eat his belly full, we will suffocate him."

Another type of assumption often used in scientific work is one that might be called assumption by default. It is very often necessary to assume a state of affairs for the simple reason that we know no better. For example, the velocity of distant stars with respect to the earth is frequently difficult to ascertain. Often the radial component can be measured spectroscopically, but the transverse component is unknown. (The situation is similar, but opposite, to the naked-eye observation of a plume of smoke on the horizon of the sea. This will soon reveal how fast the ship is moving from left to right, but not whether it is approaching or receding.) If now an astronomer needs the entire velocity of the star to calculate, say, whether some physical mechanism is feasible to explain a certain observed effect, he makes an educated guess at the velocity. Perhaps there is circumstantial evidence to suggest the order of magnitude of the velocity. To make any progress at all, he *assumes* a reasonable velocity and says so in his analysis. It is then understood that the value is very shaky, but every critic is free to check how well the proposed theory will stand up if the assumed value is in error by a factor of 10 or even 100. This type of assumption is perfectly acceptable, since it amounts to an "if. . . then" statement. However, it can also become perfectly ridiculous. Suppose the astronomer has his little pet theory which is supported only if the velocity of the star is 307.5 km/sec. If he then assumes the velocity to be exactly 307.5 km/sec on the grounds that he knows no better, neither this velocity nor his theory will be taken very seriously. This type of thing is not uncommon. All scientists are human, and many have their little pet theories and their little axes to grind. If so, they will often go looking, consciously or unconsciously, for data that support them.

This type of assumption is again very frequent in *The Limits to Growth*. The authors go to some lengths to justify it, although nobody would expect them to establish, for example, the exact dependence of birth rate on per capita GNP; for one thing there is no such exact dependence, there is at best a statistical correlation. Correlation is exactly what the word implies; it is not a cause-effect relationship. However, nobody would have blamed the authors if they had substituted a functional dependence (a curve) for the cloud of points associated with statistical correlation, and nobody would have blamed them if they had guessed at such a curve by reasonably weighing the circumstantial evidence. And this evidence is very clear. In all countries industrialization has led to higher GNP's and to lower birth rates. The actual correlation between birth rates and GNP per capita is given in *The Limits to Growth* and reproduced on p. 158 (the original source is the US Agency for International Development). At least three things are conspicuously evident from this figure. First, as common sense would predict, there is no functional relationship, only a cloud of points. Libya, for example, is far above the least-squares curve that would pass through this cloud, for the simple reason that the clique that rules it is making millions from its rich oil resources whilst the population lives in poverty and backwardness. Poverty and backwardness are known to be strongly correlated with a high birth rate, but cases like Libya, and probably Kuwait and other oil-rich countries, reduce this correlation to a fuzzy relationship between birth rate and GNP. Second, the correlation is negative for very poor countries with a per capita GNP of zero to, say, $800, that is, the birth rate has a tendency to fall with rising GNP. Third, beyond $800, the correlation is very close to zero (just like the correlation between retrograde motion of the planets and my checking account is very close to zero in all but an astrologer's opinion). If these two types of correlation are, by the crudest of approximations, replaced by a single straight line, the correlation is still negative — the birth rate decreases with rising GNP.

And so it should be, for there are some things that cannot be eliminated even by the crudest of approximations. The basic phenomenon that still transpires even through such a weird correlation as birth rate and per capita GNP is that in all cases without exception, the birth rate in industrialized countries went through a drastic reduction as these countries became industrialized. The per capita GNP is a poor measure of industrialization (as the case of Libya shows), but even so, it cannot obliterate this basic tendency which will eventually cure the underdeveloped countries of overpopulation.

The trouble is that this undeniable tendency would ruin the doomsday machine; its job is to kill the world, and overpopulation is

Figure 31 BIRTH RATES AND GNP PER CAPITA

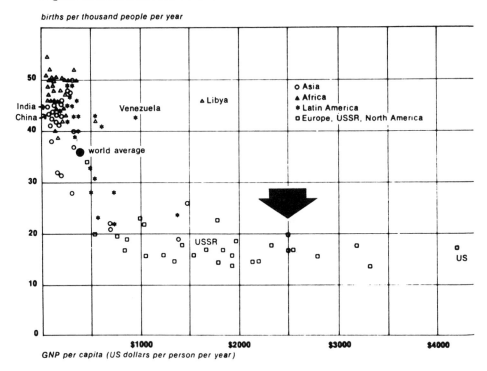

GNP per capita (US dollars per person per year)

There is no direct functional relationship between birth rates and GNP; however, there is a statistical correlation, which indicates that birth rates first decrease with rising GNP, and then there is no conspicuous dependence. The above figure bears this out, but it is used by the authors of *The Limits to Growth* to justify the next figure.

one of the important weapons in its arsenal of multiple overkill. What is needed is a dependency that goes in exactly the opposite direction: More technology means a higher per capita GNP, and a higher GNP must lead to a higher birth rate, whether the facts support it or not, because a higher birth rate is needed to kill the world; unless the curve can be bent upwards for higher GNP, the doomsday machine will not work.

Seek and ye shall find. If the facts do not provide the instrument of overkill, throw them out. Instead of the recorded birth rate, the authors introduce the "desired" birth rate, which is based on opinion surveys. Of course, it would never do to call the replacement of

Figure 32 FAMILIES WANTING FOUR OR MORE CHILDREN AND GNP PER CAPITA

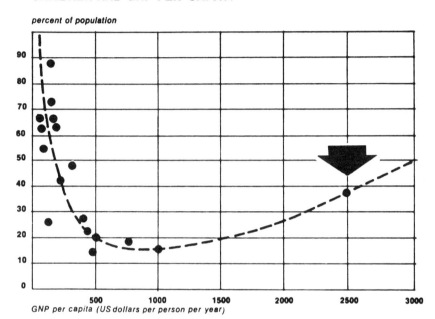

Respondents to family planning surveys in seventeen different countries indicated how many children they would like to have. The percentage of respondents desiring large families (four or more children) shows a relationship to average GNP per capita comparable to the trend shown in figure 31.

The figure and its caption are taken from *The Limits to Growth*. The points are merely opinions expressed in Gallup poll type surveys. The single point on the far right has been used to force the curve into rising with increasing GNP. The claim that this is comparable to the trend in figure 31 (opposite page) is best judged by comparing the two figures. (Note the change of scale on the GNP axis; the arrows, not contained in the originals, both point to the $2,500 value.) No rise between $1000 and $4000 is detectable in figure 31 (opposite page), but the artificially manufactured rise of the curve above is what ensures catastrophe. However, this totally unreasonable rise was apparently not fast enough, and the authors made the curve rise even faster by the manipulation shown in the next figure.

birth registers by opinion surveys the Gallup-Poll assumption; so in the days when the poor are called underprivileged and trash collectors are called ecology officers, a name for this assumption was found, too. It is the assumption of "perfect birth control." But a computer does not run on names, it runs on hard numbers fed to it by punched cards. And whatever fancy names are given to the assumption, the origin of the numbers are surveys in 17 countries, in which the respondents indicated how many children they *would like to have.*

Alas, man is a resilient animal, and not even Gallup polls can kill him; the tendency of the Gallup Poll points is still downward, less children with more income. Some more manipulation and doctoring is indicated. One of the seventeen points lies in splendid isolation from all the others; sixteen points lie between zero and $1,000 per capita GNP, then there is a long gap until a single point appears at $2,500, and that point is made to save the doomsday machine, for at last the curve can be turned upwards by the simple procedure of joining it to the last of the other points. What country is represented by this single point which has saved the day? We are not told. Judging from the $2,500 per capita GNP, it might be Switzerland, or perhaps Sweden, or perhaps Canada. Whatever the country, it must be one which, like all other countries, has shown that family size and birth rates decrease drastically as a country becomes industrialized, no matter what some dubious opinion poll may have indicated. Now compare this to the figure on p. 158 to see what the authors have ignored: no less than 24 countries, which flatly contradict the rise of the curve manufactured by the authors by picking a single, isolated point of an unknown country. Its opinion poll provides the one and only point that turns the curve upward, and this manufactured reversal of the trend is used not only in contradiction to the available evidence, but it is used for extrapolation to the whole wide world, including Uruguay, India, the Netherlands and Pago-Pago.

But even this preposterous rise in the curve is apparently not fast enough to ensure quick and efficient doom. Seek some more and ye shall find some more. And what the authors found is some economic theory which even dispenses with Gallup polls; it defines the economic value and cost of a child and the resources of a family. Divide the first by the second and multiply by the third; the resulting assortment of digits is baptized "desired family size," and this, judging from the few clues we get from the text and the flow chart, is what goes into the computer. And so it should. For at last we are

Figure 33 DESIRED FAMILY SIZE

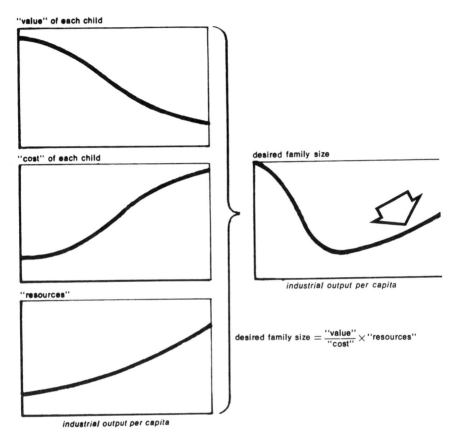

Schematic representation of the economic determinants of family size follows a rough cost-benefit analysis. The resultant curve summarizes the balance between value and cost of children and resources available for child-raising, all as a function of increasing industrialization. This composite curve is similar to the curves in figures 31 and 32.

Both the figure and the caption are taken form *The Limits to Growth*. The curve on the right is what the computer works with. Contrary to the authors' assertion, it is not at all similar to the curve in figure 31; it is, however, similar to the curve in figure 32, which has been bent against the trend shown by the facts rather than opinions. The present figure makes a parameter called "desired family size" rise even faster with industrial output, and it is this rise for large industrial outputs that causes catastrophe by overpopulation, though abundant and consistent evidence shows that family size decreases with industrial output.

home; the dependence of family size on industrial output has been doctored to rise steeply enough to guarantee another killing. The overpopulation dagger is ready to go into the arsenal of the doomsday machine.

What little curves (other than the various forms of catastrophe) are given are more confusing than enlightening. We are, for example, presented with a curve of the carbon dioxide concentration in the atmosphere which is given at once as another example of impending doom and a verification of the model. It does both of these with equal success, namely none whatsoever. The small set of data (segments, not points) of a decade have been extrapolated to an exponential covering the rest of this century in one gigantic swoop with the lavishness of a megalomaniac. The small compared segment of the curve would equally well fit the ear of Mickey Mouse or some part of the record of the Dow-Jones Industrial Average. The measurements themselves, in the magnified rectangle, are compared with the model prediction which would better have deserved the name of model postdiction. The two are set equal to each other at the beginning, so that the model is able to postdict only increases. These increases are positive and slightly growing, so that short of drawing the numbers out of a hat, most methods of approximation cannot fail to produce the approximate agreement shown in the figure. The only remarkable thing about this type of verification is that the authors give it this name without blushing.

And yet the measurements do show that the carbon dioxide concentration of the atmosphere is increasing, and this looks frightening to the man who knows little about climatology (such as myself). The source of this increasing contamination of the atmosphere, say the authors, is man's increasing combustion of fossil fuels. And they have the evidence to back them up — or do they? There is something wrong here. By rule of thumb (not always a reliable rule), man is a puny worm compared to nature, and the atmosphere bears this out like anything else. A single hurricane releases the energy of a hundred thousand hydrogen bombs. The billions of tons of water lifted from the oceans and raining down again, the billions of tons of air circulated round the globe boggle the mind. The cloud formations in the atmosphere are visible from the moon; the plume of smoke emerging from the stacks of an industrial plant cannot even be discerned from a jet plane. Half of all the carbon dioxide emitted into the air is absorbed by the oceans. 70 billion tons of carbon dioxide are absorbed annually by the vegetation of the northern

Figure 15 CARBON DIOXIDE CONCENTRATION IN THE ATMOSPHERE

parts per million by volume

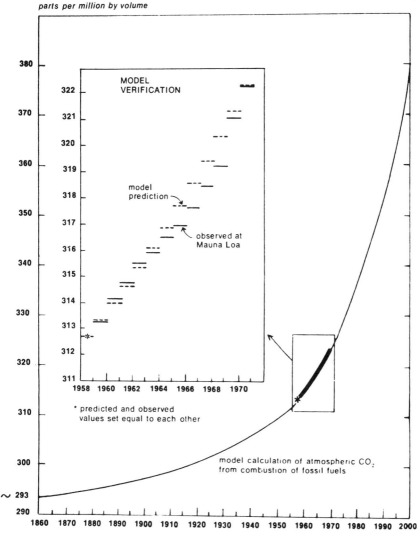

The trivial similarity between computation and observation is given the proud name of "model verification," and the curve is extrapolated in one lavish swoop to the end of this century. The measurements of carbon dioxide at Mauna Loa, Hawaii, are the only continuous and reliable measurements in the world that have been made over a prolonged period. It is unknown whether the increase measured in Hawaii is regional or worldwide, whether it is due to volcanic activity or other causes, and to what extent it is affected by the volcanic activity in Hawaii; but this is not communicated to the reader, and the increase is simply attributed to combustion of fossil fuels.

hemisphere. Such are the gigantic self-cleaning capacities of nature; even the hundreds of cubic kilometers of ash spewed into the atmosphere by the largest volcanic eruptions on record have been cleaned up by these capacities within years. Can man's puny little carbon dioxide production compete with such gigantic processes as volcanic activity? Even a non-climatologist will begin to smell a rat. And if he sniffs around long enough, he will find it: The data given in the *Limits to Growth* as one more bugaboo of doom come from Mauna Loa, Hawaii; the only place in the world where carbon dioxide concentration has been monitored reliably and continuously over a long period. There is not an ounce of evidence to suggest whether these data imply that the increase is regional or worldwide. There is not an ounce of evidence to decide whether the increase is due to man-made combustion or volcanic activity. There is not an ounce of evidence to suggest whether the volcanic activity in Hawaii influences the data more than worldwide activity.

How many more such rats are there to be sniffed out in the wheels of the doomsday machine? Must we go to the library every time the apostles of apocalypse present us with a new paper tiger?

IN discussing various types of assumptions and their abuse in *The Limits to Growth*, I have always mentioned the inductive sciences. These are the sciences that proceed by induction, from the particular to the general. The biologist goes from particular cases of white and colored peas, the circumcision of Jews, the infertility of mules, and a hundred other particular cases to the general laws of genetics. The physicist measures the density of very limited amounts of water and then, by his faith in the consistency of nature, proclaims that all water on earth, or even in the universe, attains its maximum density at 4° C.

Mathematics, which for the purposes needed here is the only *deductive* science, proceeds in the opposite direction, from the general to the particular. It is not anchored in experience, but in assumptions, and it proceeds from such general assumptions (or axioms) as "Two quantities equal to a third are equal among each other" or "No finite number can equal the sum of itself and unity" to such particular cases as that an equation of nth degree cannot have more than n roots (solutions). Truth in mathematics is not what is confirmed by experience, but what has been derived by rigorous deduction from the axioms; mathematical truths are of the type "If the following assumptions are valid, then the following theorem holds." Where the inductive sciences need only a proof beyond reasonable doubt, mathematics requires proofs beyond any doubt, however absurd or unreasonable that doubt may be. If experience were all the mathematician required, then it would be "true" that any even number equals the sum of two prime numbers ($12 = 5 + 7$, $24 = 23 + 1$, etc.), for in the two centuries that have passed since the mathematician Goldbach made this supposition, no one has yet found an even number that contradicts it, though computers can now search for such numbers by the millions. But in mathematics, experience is no proof; Goldbach's supposition will become Goldbach's theorem only after it has been proved for all even numbers to infinity, and nobody has as yet furnished such a proof. If this makes it harder on the mathematician, it also makes it easier on him in other respects. First, the physicist's truth that energy can neither be created nor destroyed holds only until someone finds an exception, and whilst it now seems absurd that such an exception will ever be found, no one can guarantee the law of the conservation of energy for the entire universe and for all eternity. There have been other laws that held for 300 years and then had to go (they were not shattered, but only modified). On the other hand, when the mathematician says "If. . .then," he has the gratifying knowledge that he is uttering a truth that will hold for all eternity. The fact that mathematics is not anchored in experience can also be turned into an advantage. True, most axioms are of the "self-evident" type. For example, Euclid's axiom that it is always possible to draw one and only one line through a point parallel to a given straight line (not passing through that point) is considered by most people as "self-evident," because what they have in mind is that if they try it with pencil and paper their experience will "confirm" it. But to a mathematician an axiom is not something to be confirmed or rejected by experience; it is something to be assumed for the system of deductions that depends on it. In fact, Riemann and other mathematicians withdrew this assumption and replaced it by the assumption that it is possible to draw more than one line through such a point. Try as you may with pencil and paper, you will never find more than one line; but experience has nothing to do with it. An entire science, called non-Euclidean geometry, rests on this new assumption which is glaringly contradicted by experience. The theorems of this science also contradict experience: The shortest distance between two points is no longer a straight line (in the conventional sense), and the angles of a triangle no longer add up to 180°. That does not mean that mathematicians are insane clowns killing time by abstract games in a non-existent world; on the contrary, Riemannian geometry has proved highly fertile in Einstein's general theory of relativity and in other disciplines that have very real applications. Similarly, the commutative law (*a* times *b* equals *b* times *a*) is assumed to hold in ordinary algebra, but not in vector algebra, matrix algebra or group theory; yet these disciplines are intensively used in all parts of physics and engineering, and their applications include such down-to-earth things as printing patterns on the textiles to be made into ladies' blouses and skirts. Mathematics simply uses truth and assumptions in a slightly different sense than the inductive sciences.

Where all this leads up to is this: Can the model used in *The Limits to Growth* not be regarded as a *mathematical* model with the assumptions made regardless of experience, the dependencies defined rather than measured, and the conclusions presented as "if. . . then" truths?

This is certainly possible. But then the doomsday machine turns into a contraption with less use than a yo-yo. First of all, it is highly unlikely that the authors of *The Limits to Growth* meant their model to be interpreted in this way, even if they call it a "mathematical" model. They would hardly have used observational data in their attempts to justify their assumptions, and they could hardly have chosen to convey a sense of urgency. You cannot withdraw Euclid's postulate and then beat the alarm that space is all crooked and the triangles won't fit it any more, and will the world please abandon Riemannian geometry while there is still time. Neither can you make a mathematically academic assumption that resources will run out in 250 years and then beat the alarm that mankind is threatened by doom. Alas, this is what the authors have done.

But we may once again disregard what the authors did or did not intend to do. It is certainly possible that some readers will interpret their work as a purely mathematical model of interplay between assumptions and conclusions. But not every such interplay is useful or even interesting. It is an unwritten law that a mathematical theorem must state something that is not immediately obvious, or at least something that cannot be proved in an obvious way. If someone proves that a circle has no corners, he will have difficulties in finding a journal that will print this discovery; on the other hand, it is not at all obvious that a game of perfect information (such as chess or ticktacktoe), in which both players know the results of all moves made previously, has one and only one optimum strategy, which will always lead to the same result (win, lose or draw). That theorem is, in fact, one of the basic theorems of the theory of games. But if the *Limits to Growth* computer programs are understood as a purely mathematical model, what do they prove? That if population grows faster than the food supply, the population will eventually starve. Who needs a computer for that? That if pollution increases with population and technology, and if both do increase, people will eventually suffocate in filth. Who needs a computer for that? That if resources last only 250 years, they will be gone in 250 years. Who needs a computer for that? The only thing that might possibly be of interest in such trivialities is exactly when the inevitable end must come; but the authors have made it very plain that such details are of no interest and that they are interested only in tendencies, not in exact details (which, in itself, is a reasonable attitude, and no one will blame them for it).

What the doomsday machine proves, in effect, is that if you have no other means of subsistence than a box of poisoned candy, then you are doomed. If you clean out the poison, you will eventually come to the bottom of the box and starve; if you don't, you will be poisoned; if there is more of you to eat out of the box, the bottom will be reached sooner; if you eat faster, you will reach the bottom sooner, if you eat more slowly, you will reach it later. Who needs a computer to derive such trivialities?

But this a-killer-at-each-exit game remains equally trivial whether regarded as a strictly mathematical model or not. All it does is confuse the issues. Exponential growth cannot continue in a closed system forever, say the authors, and they run a computer to prove a point that every sane man must concede. But who says that all growth is exponential and that it will be stopped only by catastrophe? Not the statistics. If pollution is allowed to grow unchecked, we shall all eventually suffocate; the computer obediently confirms this triviality. But the point is that pollution can be checked by more and better technology, as confirmed by theory and experiment, but contradicted by the warped curves fed into the doomsday machine.

250 years' worth of resources will run out in 250 years; earlier if the present rate goes up, and later if it is curbed. The demonstration of this profound wisdom was not performed by Don Quixote because he lived in the age of windmills and not computers. But who says resources are limited? Where are the input data saying that demand on one type of resource ceases when a new type is discovered or

synthesized? Where do they say that copper can be, and is already being, replaced by aluminum and that neither copper nor aluminum will be required for ever? Where do they take account of the resources being replaced by synthetic materials?

Similarly, food supplies are, at the moment, increasing faster than population, not only in the United States, but worldwide. Except, of course, in the warped assumptions of the doomsday machine and the literature of the ecocult. But at least the literature of the ecocult arrived at exactly the same conclusions without wasting costly computer time. How come? Why was a computer program needed to arrive at false conclusions from false assumptions? Was it because a soothsayer needs a crystal ball, not for saying the sooth, but to impress his clients? Was it because people today are more impressed by computers and systems theory than by witches' cauldrons?

But the doomsday machine is not only trivial, it is also unstable. It suffers from such a dose of overkill that its designers, try as they might, are unable to save it from self-destruction. It is not too late to save the world, we are told. Look, the whole thing of punched cards can be stabilized into a state of world equilibrium: The print-out shows curves where pollution is much the same as it is today, and the per capita food is not radically increased from its present value where about half the world goes hungry. We must stop industrial output at its 1975 levels, pass from capital investments to consumer goods, and meddle with a couple's business of how many children they want to have, and we shall approach this semi-paradise of semi-clean air and semi-fed people. Alas, the authors' dream is not even a semi-dream, for their assumptions lead from this semi-paradise to total disaster. The designers of the doomsday machine forgot to fit it with a reverse gear, and their assumptions have painted them into a corner from which they will still see the bottom of the poisoned candy box. Their assumptions made resources finite and limited, and no doctoring and manipulation will prevent the resources curve from running down, down, down. You can eat the candy more slowly, but eventually you will still reach the bottom of the box. This profound wisdom is again confirmed by the computer simulations, and though the authors try to stabilize their world of punched cards hither and thither, the resources curve goes inexorably down to doom. The doomsday machine cannot be undoomed. All the authors have to say about this is contained in four lines out of the whole book. "That limit is very far in time if resources are managed wisely," they advise us. Their "time horizon" is only

Figure 47 STABILIZED WORLD MODEL II

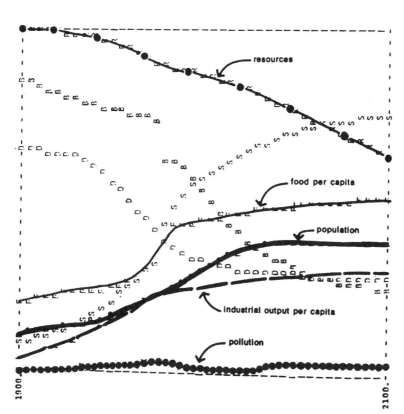

A world model recommended by the authors of *The Limits to Growth*. The per capita food consumption has not risen very drastically over today's levels, when half the world goes hungry. Industrial output stagnates at roughly its present value, and pollution levels are about the same as now. Apparently such a world will eventually be put out of its misery by the rapidly declining resources.

70 years, and apparently doom in 200 or 400 years is not the real doom they have in mind; delayed doom is undoomed doom.

In 1893, the London *Daily Express* printed a report about a man who wanted to commit suicide with no chance of staying alive.* He took poison and attempted to shoot himself in the head while hanging himself from a high cliff above the sea, for he could not swim. But as he jumped, the shot missed and tore the rope; he fell into the sea and swallowed much brine, which neutralized the poison, and the sea washed him ashore alive. The doomsday machine leaves no such small chances; it guarantees suicide under all conditions, and not even its designers can stop it when they try. The doomsday machine is a dud.

CONSIDER next the meaning of a "model." The original meaning of the word, when used in science, was somewhat different than it is today. It referred to a laboratory arrangement which was usually quite different from the object under study, but it obeyed the same type of equations. For example, the equation that governs the bending of a radio ray in the atmosphere is (except for numerical values, which can be accounted for) the same as that governing the profile of a soap bubble formed between two circular wire rings; the radii of the rings correspond to the antenna heights, and the profile of the bubble to the trajectory of the ray. It is easier to examine the behavior of a soap bubble in the laboratory than a radio ray in the atmosphere; the former can be used as a model for the latter. There are many other such examples, such as electrical small-scale models of geological formations, but in general, this type of modeling has been displaced by computer simulations and computer solutions of the equations which were being solved on the analogue model.

More often today, the word *model* implies not so much an analogue, but a simplified duplicate of the mechanism under study. Often the mechanism is unknown and the idea of the model is to produce the same effects as the ones observed in the original, which makes it likely that the two mechanisms are similar. In searching for this similarity, scientists do not attempt to reproduce every little detail, for they are usually only interested in the basic mechanisms of the original. The authors of *The Limits to Growth* are, in my opinion, entirely blameless from this point of view. They cannot be expected to produce a model that duplicates all known (and unknown) dependencies exactly, and their attitude of looking for ten-

---

* I read it in the "Fifty Years Ago" column in 1943.

dencies, not the details, is reasonable; it is regretable that they do not keep to this attitude when it comes to the supposed resource depletion in a shorter or longer interval. Their (and Forrester's) claim that everybody has a mental model of the world in his head might perhaps be better discussed by philosophers, but basically I see nothing wrong with it, since it only amounts to a little more stretching of the meaning of the word.

But there are other objections to their computer model. The most conspicuous shortcoming is that its behavior is not at all similar to the real world, and if the behavior of a model does not agree with that of the original, it is often used as a demonstration that the assumptions that went into the model are false. The doomsday machine does not resemble the behavior of the real world even remotely. The checks and balances of nature, the ecocult's slogans to the contrary, are not in the least delicate, and the few natural catastrophies that have occured could hardly be caused by anything as insignificant as man. Man can exterminate the buffalo or the whale and he can release enough energy at one time to kill 100,000 of his own species as he did in Hiroshima, he can kill the marine life in this river or that lake, but when it comes to real catastrophies, he is still an impotent worm. A single hurricane releases more energy than one hundred thousand hydrogen bombs, and all the pollutants of all the cars on a continent are like a breeze of fresh air compared to a major outburst of a volcano. The checks and balances of nature are anything but delicate. When an overmature forest is ready to die, lightning will set it alight and burn the young and healthy trees together with the old and diseased ones; eventually, by crude randomness, biased probabilities and the law of large numbers, a few young and healthy trees surviving the fire will result in a new forest. When nature changes a species by mutation, she does so by the same lavish randomness; most of the more viable will make it, and most of the less viable will die out in a gigantic and crude struggle for survival. Billions of tons of water are raised from the oceans and released to rain down again; billions of tons of air are circulated around the globe; forces that we do not yet understand change the magnetic field of the entire globe and cause rythms of its ice ages. To think that all this could be changed to an extent where mankind almost vanishes from the earth by not accepting the conclusions of *The Limits to Growth* is ludicrous and arrogant. The cataclysms of pollution shown in the print-outs have no resemblance to the slight and slow interaction between man and nature; they are so drastically different that the objection "There's always a first time" will not bridge the abyss.

Something similar is evidently true of human society, though its mechanisms are even more poorly understood than those of nature. Society appears to have built-in protective devices that work well enough without advice from unrealistic computer models. If society does approach disaster, it does so slowly, giving itself time for countermeasures; whether these countermeasures take the form of administrative action, economic necessity, or even revolution, migration, or any others makes little difference to the point. The historical evidence suggests that society is growing more resilient to upheavals and threatening disasters. Man survived the ice age without technology of any kind; plagues and famines decimated the population much more than such relatively minor upheavals as the French or Russian revolution. People will stand by indifferently whilst seals and whales (and their own kind) are being slaughtered, but they will not, in the long run, permit the air to be polluted until they all die. Society simply does not stand by dying and watching such cataclysms as depicted in *The Limits to Growth*, however much people may enjoy reveling in masochistic thrills whilst regarding the print-outs on paper. The countermeasures need not take a consciously organized form; nobody organized to substitute aluminum for copper in some countries, it simply became an economic necessity. Nobody organized engineers to replace metal gears by synthetic material; they recognized its superior properties. Nobody organized people to have two children instead of twelve; they knew that all children would probably survive, and they could not afford to send twelve children to college. It took the Turks 300 years to ruin the Balkans by depleting its forests; but even there a feedback loop led to the result that this type of mismanagement reduced the powerful Turkish Empire to almost nothing, whilst better managed societies displaced it. This line of reasoning, alas, does not work for nuclear wars; however, this possibility is not considered in *The Limits to Growth*, and I will not consider it in this connection either. But what the model does consider leads to behavior so unlike that of nature and society that this behavior alone would raise grave suspicions that the assumptions are false; as it is, it merely confirms their falseness found by direct examination. A useful model need not reproduce all the details of the original, but it must at least resemble some of the tendencies of its behavior. A canary will never work as a model of the solar system.

The attempt of the authors of the *Limits to Growth* to make their model represent the entire world is no less than fantastic. The various loops linking their state variables are rendered entirely ficti-tious by this claim. It is not only unrealistic to apply curves manipu-lated mostly from the data of the advanced countries to the 80% or so of the rest of the world, but most of the relationships built into the doomsday machine simply do not exist on a worldwide basis, and in this sense it is futile to argue whether they are right or wrong. As far as its system levels and other variables are concerned, we do not yet live in one world. Industrial air pollution is worst in Japan, America and Europe. Rapid population growth now exists only in South America, Africa and Asia. If the feedback loops and other interconnections of the doomsday machine were anything but a fic-tion, population growth in these parts of the world would lead to an increase of pollution in the industrialized countries, until it became so bad that the population in the underdeveloped countries stopped growing because the car exhausts of Los Angeles would shorten the life span of the inhabitants of Rawalpindi. If the doomsday machine were not a ludicrous contraption for the many other reasons, this principle alone would expose it as nonsensical. And this principle is repeated in loop after loop, for the authors chose to take on no less than the entire world. Does shortage of food in India stop capital investment in the United States? Does pollution in Tokyo reduce the per capita food consumption in Venezuela? Communications, trans-port and other advances of technology have indeed shrunk the world and increased the interdependence of its various parts, but there is still a long way to go before we live in one world where cause and effect are closely linked between Detroit and Zambia. At present, these links are weak, and one such link is that a Zambian will take as kindly to the idea of limiting industrial growth as a Haarlemite takes kindly to the idea that the trouble with the world is too much prosperity. The worldwide links between cause and effect as postu-lated in the doomsday machine are nonexistent. This, of course, is nothing new; the erroneous pairing of cause and effect is as old as mankind. It is called superstition.

Causality is not the strong point of the authors. The text accom-panying their print-outs leaves one in doubt as to whether they have a good understanding of the difference between a mathematical correlation on one hand, and cause and effect on the other. They have mistaken the temporary correlation between industrial growth and pollution for a universal cause-effect relationship. They have ignored the evidence of industrial growth accompanied by decreasing air pollution that can now be observed in the United States.

Such errors in mistaking statistical correlations for cause-effect relationships can lead to the most absurd paradoxes. In Japan, pollution has been on the increase since World War II faster than in any other country. At the same time, the average height of the Japanese has been remarkably on the increase; not because of pollution, but because of an increasingly protein-rich diet. Had the authors plotted pollution in Japan against the average height of its inhabitants, they would have obtained a very clear positive correlation and a convincingly rising curve that could be fitted to the data. Does that mean that pollution in Japan can be stopped by hormone injections that will keep the Japanese small? Can their growth be stunted by curbing pollution?

If the doomsday machine were not a doomsday machine, but a realistic model of the interrelations between man and his environment, it could still only yield interrelations; it could be helpful in discovering some causalities, but it could not provide them by itself.

There is another point on which the authors of *The Limits to Growth* have been criticized. In some book reviews it has been pointed out that the assumption "if present trends continue" is mistaken, and if it were true, all Americans would eventually become heroin addicts. But on this point I must, with admitted reluctance, take the authors' side. This type of faulty prediction results when a curve (such as that of rising heroin addiction) is extrapolated by prolonging it into the future in accordance with certain rules that take account of its properties in the past. This is a very crude method of prediction, and the authors of *The Limits to Growth* have used it only in some of the input data which the computer processes. The actual processing is based on a method pioneered by J.W. Forrester, in which no such crude methods are used. It does not correspond to the curves characteristic of functional relationships, but to small changes characteristic of many interdependent differential equations. A differential equation, to sacrifice accuracy for briefness, is a relation between the slope, curvature and other characteristics of a curve at any of its points, and the problem is to find the entire curve. If the same method (called System Dynamics) were applied to model the rate of heroin addiction in a country, it would have to take account of the factors influencing it (perhaps death rate from heroin, profit of the pushers, law enforcement against them, pressures for and against initial use, and very many others). The resulting curve of heroin addiction would then, presumably, not rise so high as to include the entire population. Except for the input characteristics, therefore, this criticism of *The Limits to Growth* is not justified. It boils down to the same story as before: There is nothing wrong with systems theory or modeling; it is the model itself which is entirely unacceptable.

As far as mathematical techniques are concerned, another point is far more damning, and that is the authors' use of nonlinearities. It is not easy to define what a system is, but for the present purposes is will perhaps suffice to say that it is something which can be "excited" by an input to respond with one or several outputs. In an amplifying system, the input is the speaker's voice, the output is the sound coming from the loudspeakers. A cow can be regarded as a system with grass as its input and milk one of its outputs. The input and output need not have separate entrance and exit doors; for example, a steel bar undergoing tests for tensile strength can be regarded as a system with the tensile force as input and the resulting prolongation as output. A linear system is one whose output is proportional to its input. If you speak twice as loud into the microphone, the loudspeakers will also produce sound twice as loud. If you give a cow 10% more grass, it will produce roughly 10% more milk. If you double the force on a steel bar, the stress will also double. But only within reason. Linear systems are an abstraction, because systems are approximately linear only within small ranges. If you force 200 lb of grass into a cow, you will not get more milk, you will kill the cow. If you keep increasing the input to a microphone, which is most easily done by a feedback loop letting the sound from the loudspeaker go straight into the microphone, you will achieve an earsplitting squeal, but you cannot raise the sound level any further. If you increase the force on a steel bar beyond a certain value, the stress will begin to grow rapidly and then stop altogether, because you will have torn the bar.

All of these phenomena are, in a sense, catastrophies, and any catastrophy must be associated with a nonlinearity of the system; things do not go on as they used to, the input-output characteristic is no longer a straight line, it bends and eventually reaches a saturation level, or it stops altogether because the system has been ruined. Conversely, if a model produces catastrophies for which there is no reasonable expectation, then the place to look for the error is in the nonlinearities of the input-output characteristics of the subsystems which are linked together in the model.

Each of the 100 or so labels on the flow diagram of the doomsday machine represents a subsystem for which an input-output characteristic is needed if the machine is to run. There are none among them for which the exact relationship is known, for even such simple relations as population increase equals births minus deaths is only part of the input and output of a subsystem labeled "Total Population." It is also linked to such things as "Urban-Industrial Land Required" and "Crowding." In some cases, there may have been data to guide the authors, though what little insight they give us on this point does them little credit. The remaining characteristics of these subsystems, which require characteristics of such bewildering dependencies as birth control effectiveness on service output per capita, or land yield on pollution, are surely hard to come by from any reputable source, and the chances are that the authors simply decreed them. These relationships, or many of them, must be non-linear, or the whole system could not end in catastrophe, but what exactly they are is not communicated to the reader, except for a handful of examples (three, to be precise; some more to illustrate the authors' reasoning rather than to show what actually went into the program). One of these examples is the characteristic that produces a number called "desired family size" as a function of industrial output per capita. The unreasonable rise of this curve has been discussed before, and if I return to it now in connection with nonlinearities, it is only because the authors have not included the characteristics of the other subsystems of the doomsday machine. The usual type of nonlinearity, saturation or stabilization at some level, is not sufficient in this case to guarantee catastrophe, and the nonlinearity had to be pushed into a reversal of the trend, which was done by running the Gallup poll curve through the totally untypical point of some arbitrarily selected country (p.159). Even the objection of no other opinion polls being available is easily refuted, and by the authors themselves. This is not the only case providing a point that does not conform to the general tendency, and in these other cases the authors knew better than to run the curve through such an outlayer. It is this nonlinearity which causes catastrophe through overpopulation, and whilst in other cases a little bending here or there is unimportant for what is essentially groping in the dark, it is inexcusable in this case, when the bending supplies the mechanism that produces the catastrophe. You cannot prove the presence of human saliva in the mummies of Egyptian pharaoes by spitting into them.

There is another interesting aspect of this suicide path from industry to overpopulation. The flow chart in *The Limits to Growth* shows the shortest path between industrial output and population (omitting unessential delay boxes) proceeding via industrial output per capita, desired birth-multiplier from industrial output, desired birth rate, fertility and birth rate to total population. The reader is offered only a glimpse of the relationships programmed for this path, namely the nonlinearity of the desired birth rate, and this is the one where the curve has been turned back until contrary to all available evidence it says that birth rates increase with industrial output. In this way more industry evidently guarantees suicide by overpopulation. But the curve keeps on rising, and how is the poor computer to know that it should not make women give birth to 20 children a month if the industrial output becomes sufficiently high? It knows nothing about pregnancies or the other facts of life, and the positive slope of the curve would have to turn human couples into high-speed child producing automata ("It won't take long, dear, did it?"). We are not told exactly how this population super-explosion by industrial output is prevented, but we get another glimpse from the flow chart. It shows a sink attached to the fertility box and labeled "maximum biological birth rate." In other words, if the fantastic assumption leads to fantastic results, instruct the computer not to store them in its memory locations. Prevent absurd fertilities not by realistic inputs, but by an automatic censor. Then take the results to the public and beat the alarm.

The nonlinearity of resource usage is of a quite different type. Here the authors use an S-shaped curve which ends in saturation. But whilst Forrester in *World Dynamics* uses a similarly shaped curve for the rate of depletion, he gives a very different reason for it: "Much of modern capital investment, which here is assumed to include research and the store of knowledge and education, does not deplete resources." This line of thinking, had it been continued, might have revealed that resources continue to be available by replacement, synthetic production and other means constantly bred by advancing technology. But this unfinished line of reasoning is not adopted in *The Limits to Growth*. Here, the saturation rate is merely used to deplete the finite box of candy, and the shape of the curve is taken from world steel consumption. Steel is no longer considered an all-embracing indicator of industrial production; it is being replaced by other materials in many applications, and if steel consumption ever reaches zero, the chances are that the reason will not be that there is no more iron ore, but that it is no longer needed.

To all this, one gathers, the reply is "If you have a better model, let's see it." In *World Dynamics*, Forrester says as much in words to that effect, and one senses the same attitude in *The Limits to Growth*. But there are two fallacies in this reply. The first is that by all accepted customs, the burden of proof is on those who state what is not at all obvious. I cannot merely proclaim that a yo-yo is a somewhat imperfect model of the alternation of ice ages and if you don't think so, go build something better. Much less can I use a yo-yo to beat the alarm that another ice age is coming.

The other point is that most scientists probably *could* set up a better model given the money that the Club of Rome and the Volks-wagenstiftung shelled out for this purpose, though it is doubtful whether many would have the grandiose spirit of attempting to put the entire world into a computer program of a few hundred lines; they might suggest tackling a smaller unit first. Most scientists are now familiar with computer programming, which is becoming ever easier as technology develops. System dynamics is also a very simple way of simulating the behavior of a system of many differential equations, in fact, from this point of view, *The Limits to Growth* do no more than inflate the method used in *World Dynamics* by a large number of additional variables and unreliable or arbitrary dependencies between them. When I say that system dynamics is "simple," this is meant as a favorable property, not as an attempt to belittle it, for many discoveries are simple — after they are made.

Given these tools, it appears highly probable that most scientists could work out more realistic, if less ambitious, models of interactions between society and environment. Such models would hardly produce catstrophies under all conditions, and they would therefore arouse less publicity; but publicty and sensationalism is not the object of science. Another question is whether many scientists would *want* to get involved in such projects. Most of them have too little time and money for the projects on which they are now engaged, and they might not wish to spend time and money, both of which are hard to come by, on improving a crystal ball.

IN MOST of this chapter, a parallel has been drawn between the scientific approach and the approach that transpires from the *Limits to Growth*. In this connection, another point should perhaps be mentioned. Scientific findings cannot be changed by likes and dislikes, faiths or ideologies. A scientist cannot let his opinions, his preferences, his religion or his ideology interfere with his scientific work for the simple reason that there is no such thing as "his" science. I have, in the foregoing discussion, left little doubt that I dislike the apocalyptic thinking which is apparent in *The Limits to Growth*; but if the programs were well founded in the facts and the deductions were clean, I would have to accept the conclusions whether I liked them or not. I reject the conclusions not because I dislike them, but because they are based on false and arbitrary assumptions and manipulated nonlinearities, and because they are even inconsistent with the results such a meaningless model has produced. The mixing of scientific research with personal beliefs, on the contrary, raises the question whether the authors of *The Limits to Growth* have not become entrapped in the doomsday philosophy until, consciously or not, they produced a model of the world that conforms to it. I have no doubt that they sincerely believe that the curves they have produced are meaningful, but sincerity is not the point under discussion. Who cares whether the scientists who rejected evolution on the grounds that it contradicted the Bible were sincere? What mattered in the long run was that Darwin was right and they were wrong. Who cares whether Lysenko was sincere when he claimed that Mendelian genetics was false because it contradicted the teachings of communism? What mattered in the long run was that communist genetics were no match against scientific genetics.

But whilst the good intentions of the authors are of little interest to the factual issue, the effect of their book cannot be denied. *The Limits to Growth* have spawned a litter of smaller doomsday machines which can now be found proliferating in engineering and computer science departments of reputable universities. If the assumptions of the mother doomsday machine are preposterous, those of her litter are often hair-raising. Time was when astrology gave birth to astronomy, and alchemy gave birth to chemistry. In our age, apocalyptic holocaustology is giving birth to computerized bamboozlery.

No longer do you need black sows to be slaughtered by the light of the midnight moon to gaze into the future; entrails of oxen, tea-leaves, dead cats, crystal balls and gypsy fortune tellers are old hat: Ph.D.'s are now saying the sooth with the digital computer. No more cemeteries or secret sabbaths round the witch's cauldron: The seances are now being held in the halls of higher learning.

I do not question the honesty of the computerized soothsayers and magicians of electronic witchcraft tending the litter of the mother doomsday machine.

What I question is their competence.

6

The Phosphate Phlop and Other Phoolishness

Subject to a single major exception, it appears that a shift from phosphate detergents to soap in both eutrophied and non-eutrophied areas will normally benefit the environment. That exception is the case where (1) the additional use of the soap will aggravate a known Biological Oxygen Demand problem and (2) eutrophication is neither present nor imminent.

Advice to Consumers on Laundry Detergents, Report to the Senate Committee on Commerce, December 1971.

Crying wolf too often benefits nobody except the wolf.

In some respects, the present environmental hysteria is reminiscent of the McCarthy hysteria in the fifties. Then, as now, the most absurd accusations were leveled at the most laughable targets, and the most absurd remedies were proposed, and sometimes even enforced, to thwart a danger in places where none existed. President Eisenhower was called a communist stooge; the State Department was allegedly run by an organized communist conspiracy; folk singers were communists, all of them; US customs confiscated some 19th century classics as subversive literature; cangoroo hearings smeared innocent people who had no recourse; and this hysteria was not merely fanned by Senator McCarthy and right-wing organizations, but large sections of the country were gripped by it.

The effects of this crusade against a subversion that never materialized are all too apparent. If someone now points to the dangers, not of a discredited and obsolete ideology, but of Soviet imperialism and its lust for conquest, he is dismissed as an alarmist, if not as a warmonger and fascist. That kind of talk has been heard too often. Nobody, for example, believed that the Soviets would invade Czechoslovakia, let alone a few days after they had signed a new treaty with its communist government. A mere four years later, this episode is now largely forgotten. The Soviets have abandoned the idea of world revolution, it is believed, and "therefore" they pose no immediate threat to the United States; if somebody points out, for example, the consistently increasing capability of the Soviets to cut off America's oil supplies, he is often regarded as a member of the rightist lunatic fringe.

Ecohysteria is a close parallel in the exercise of crying wolf. Paul Ehrlich's horror fiction, the call to save the environment from flood control, opposition to urgently needed power stations, calls for de-development and the rest of the drivel may eventually make people indifferent to the idea that air and water pollution should be stopped and eliminated, and a point may be reached when pollution becomes overwhelming. The gurus of the ecocult will then, no doubt, exclaim with smug satisfaction "We told you so!"

Such a regretable process is not only unwittingly promoted by the environmental fanatics, but it is also liable to be helped by other circumstances. It is easier to blame the Demons of Detroit for all the pollution than to pay the bill for pollution control devices. When polluting plants are closed down, as the environmentalists have already discovered, the biggest uproar comes not from big business, but from the labor unions, who want the jobs for their members. An energy crisis in some form can now hardly be avoided, and when the blackouts hit, people will naturally want power for their refrigerators first, and for the water treatment plants second or hundred and second. They may clamor for more electric power as fast as power plants can be buit, and that means fossil burning plants. Nitrogen oxides and particulate pollutants may then well be thrown into one bag with Ehrlich's horror fiction. When "environmental" bills are introduced for lavish federal funding to preserve "wilderness" areas in order to safeguard the homes of the affluent who are already living there, the less affluent will side with the developers, and the builders, pavers and bulldozer drivers will become custodians of the environment. A rational middle road never has much chance in a tight spot.

Yet the dangers of pollution are very real, and the environmental fanatics not only bring them nearer by their action directed against pollutionless technology, they also make light of them by their horror fiction which must sooner or later fall flat on its face. The greatest pollution to be found at present is not in American cities, but in the cities of Japan, and it has already led to diseases unknown in other countries. Like the disease of rickets, which was not widespread before the industrial revolution, but became known in Europe as "the English disease," so the diseases *minamata* and *itai-itai* may retain their names because the Japanese were the first to contract them.

But who is going to take *minamata* or *itai-itai* seriously after Paul Ehrlich's sick tales about unattended people coughing out their lives in front of New York hospitals?* Who will believe in any more danger after the two hundredth prediction of the environmental fanatics has turned out to be another silly hoax? Who will believe, even now, that anything can be done after various college professors have said that it is too late already?

Of course, most Americans are not exactly panicking in the face of silly computer print-outs or fables about drodystrophic dwarfism. But when housewives are made fools of by being told to switch from one kind of detergent to another and then to switch back again, they may not heed other warnings even if they are true. And New England farmers and landowners who have seen hundreds of thousands of wooded acres denuded by insects after DDT was banned are likely to throw other pesticides around by the ton while the going is good.

PHOSPHATES

Ecologists, of all people, should know that "useful" and "harmful" are very relative concepts. Long before the word *ecology* lost its meaning, J.B.S. Haldane and Konrad Lorenz taught that there was no such thing as useful and harmful animals, there is only a balance

---

* See p. 31. For details of "The Great Die-Off" of the 1970's in the United States, see *Looking Backward from 2000 A.D.*, by Paul R. Ehrlich, The Progressive, vol. 34, no. 4, pp. 23-25, April 1970. Here Ehrlich's visions kill 125 million Americans by some virus, another 65 million by famine, and more by reactor disasters, leucemia, drodystrophic dwarfism, and other killers not yet thought of by lesser minds. Such genocidal orgies are not without result to the issue closest to the author's heart. The government of the United States ("of North America") in the year 2,000 has a Division of Optimum Population.

in nature which is kept up by the interplay of all species. The "useful" animals are useless unless the "harmful" ones make themselves useful by providing them with food, and the vice-versas up and down the food chains make utter nonsense out of "useful" and "harmful." But that is not the way the latter-day ecologists look at things. Like all super-simplifiers, they delight in good-or-bad dichotomies. Phosphates are bad. Soap is good. Technology is bad. Organic foods are good. Pesticides are bad. The bicycle is good. Cars are bad. Please memorize.

In the late sixties, phosphates were very bad. The outcry reached such proportions that by 1970 every civic-minded housewife spurned Tide, Fab, Dash, Cheer, All, and the rest of the stuff that washes whiter than white, 10 feet tall and they even smell better gets out the worst kind of dirt. She turned to detergents that were quite harmless to both the environment and the dirt in the laundry, though they manifested their super-duper strength on her eyes and hands, and they made her inflammable clothes flammable. She is now using phosphates again.

Phosphates are unconnected with an earlier problem caused by detergents, which has been solved by improved technology. Detergents used to make persistent suds in streams and other waters which they eventually reached after flowing out from the sinks and washing machines. Pressed by legislators and others, the detergent manufacturers resisted and declared the problem unsolvable, but as is probably about to happen with the rotary engine and its emission controls, manufacturers will quickly change their stand when threatened by competition from a more advanced company, and in this case German chemical companies were about to introduce biodegradable detergents, which are broken up by natural processes in the environment. This, and the threats of Congress to legislate against persistent detergents, made US manufacturers turn round, and since 1965, nothing but biodegradable detergents have been manufactured. Probably banking on the fact that this is unknown to most housewives, one company advertises its detergents not as *super-duper* or *fantastic*, but as *biodegradable*, as if the other detergents were not.

Phosphates are not the ingredients that do the actual washing in the powder sold in the various boxes with the fancy names. The actual removal of dirt from the fabric is done by the detergent proper, called surfactant. The other ingredients, called "builders," merely support this activity. The job of phosphates is to soften the water so as to keep the removed dirt in suspension and prevent its redeposition on the fabric and in the washing machine; they enable the dirt to flow away with the water when the wash is rinsed. They are not the only ingredients that can do this job; there are many other chemicals (such as caustic soda) that will soften the water, but the others are less effective and have all types of side effects, such as forming a crust of deposits in the washer or breaking down the layer that impregnates fabrics to make them flameproof. They are also health hazards. No better ingredient than phosphates has as yet been found to do the job and to be as free of side effects. The second best thing is probably the installation of a water softener, which costs from $250 up and requires attendance, such as refilling its container with 200 lbs of salt every two or three months.

But phosphates are also nutrients for plants, animals and people. For plants, they act as fertilizers second only to nitrates. If water is rich in phosphates, it will under some, but not all, conditions supply food to algae, microscopic organisms (plants) that live in water and give it the green color often seen in still, shallow waters or in the water of an aquarium that has not been well tended to. Phosphates are not the only nutrients algae live on, but under certain conditions, they will so fertilize them that the algae will proliferate to an extent that becomes a nuisance, though no direct threat to human health is involved. Such an overfertilization with nutrients, in which lakes or other standing waters become clogged with algae, is known as eutrophication.

It is not, however, the live algae that cause problems; on the contrary, like any other plant, they produce oxygen through photosynthesis. The trouble is caused by the dead algae, which not only produce bad odors and wash ashore in the form of a smelly slime, but which create a "biological oxygen demand" (BOD). The decomposition of dead algae provokes bacterial activity, and this is what creates the oxygen demand. This, of course, happens with any type of dead organic matter, not only with dead algae. The resulting biological oxygen demand can deprive other aquatic life, such as certain fish, of an adequate oxygen supply and if eutrophication is sufficiently severe, it can decimate the stock of fish in standing waters, or even eliminate it altogether.

This part of the story became known, in part, through the cases where it actually happened, but mainly through the outcry of the instant ecologists, which was loud enough to give any housewife using Tide or most other things doing a good job on the laundry a staggering guilt complex. By 1969, the new crusade was in full swing.

No longer did the environmental fanatics shout murder and pestilence. Eutrophication and biological oxygen demand became the watchwords of the new crusade, and housewives could not but capitulate in the face of such terrible words. You do not have to understand such words as eutrophication, convolution of holomorphic functions or degenerate conic sections to get the jitters; the sound alone is enough to give you the creeps. The first to join the holy crusade was the econuts' obsequious devil, big business; prodded by the Department of the Interior, they sank millions into the development of a phosphate substitute and came up with NTA (sodium nitrilotriacetate). Little did Proctor & Gamble know that it would have to write off $7,100,000 in binding contracts to purchase NTA when the government later told them quietly to lay off it again. Other companies were no less obsequious. One food store chain decorated its supermarkets with giant streamers "Let's Be Eco-Logical" and displayed giant tables of the phosphate percentages in various detergents down to Dash, which (according to these tables) contained the largest amount. Probably never before did a business advertise the equivalent of "Please don't buy our goods." Smaller business was very quick to capitalize on the new fad. Ground bricks mixed with cow dung would presumably have sold by the ton in those days, except perhaps for the phosphates in the cow dung. However, some companies went back to the old washing soda and to soap, which also causes problems of biological oxygen demand. New detergents appeared on the shelves, and the housewife could buy them without guilt or fear, for they had such names as Un-Polluter, Ecolo-G, Concern and Pure Water. Ecolo-G, made by the Ecology Corporation of America, gained a full 10% of the crowded detergent market, and what exactly it had in the cartons imprinted with Ecolo-G I do not know; but it was something that seriously disturbed the Food and Drug Administration, for it was found to be toxic, corrosive to the skin, and the cause of severe eye irritation.

The new detergents gave algae little food and the laundry little cleanness, and at first it seemed that they were totally harmless, whether to dirt, algae or anything else. That soon proved an illusion. It did not help the environment much, because to get the laundry something like clean, housewives had to use much larger quantities of the corresponding effi-G. Soap, too, is an organic material which creates biological oxygen demand in sewage treatment plants, many of which partly depend on bacterial decomposition; certainly septic tanks depend on it entirely. One of the things that the instant ecologists did not know was that many industrial plants had, years ago, been criticized for creating too much biological oxygen demand by their large scale use of soap, and the problem was only solved by switching to detergents.

But the change in menu for the bacteria was no longer the most worrying point. The carbonates, metasilicates, and the other caustic ingredients of the new detergents caused irritation of nose membranes, skin irritation, eye irritation, and in some cases, serious eye damage. In the summer of 1971, a fifteen-month-old girl died in Connecticut after inhaling (not eating) a quantity of the new type of detergent where phosphates had been replaced by caustic substances. It was also found that washing-soda detergents could inactivate the flameproof finishes on clothing. The story, or rather one half of it, had started with algae and had now progressed to the danger of people being burned alive.

Toward the end of 1970 and most of 1971, things were highly confused. A former Secretary of the Interior appeared in television commercials for Sears & Roebuck recommending their non-phosphate detergent "for our water's sake." At the same time Sears & Roebuck's Kenmore washers came with leaflets warning users that phosphate-free detergents leave a scaly build-up, interfere with the washer's mechanism and cause abrasion or wear of fabrics as they rub against the agitator. In many displays, the ecology-minded detergent was proudly placed next to a Kenmore washer. But this was as nothing compared to the confusion in Washington. "*You* get *us* off the hook!" the detergent makers and the government were shouting at each other. Government is perhaps too strong a word to use. The Interior Department and its water-quality agency, as late as May 1970, demanded an immediate cut in phosphates, and other federal officials, prodded by the House conservation and natural resources committee, exhorted the manufacturers to change to NTA. But the Commisioner of the Federal Water Pollution Control Administration had declared that the reduction or elimination of phosphorus was "desirable in concept," but that it could cause "other, even more severe, pollutional effects." In December 1970, the Department of Health, Education and Welfare called a meeting with the representatives of the detergent industry. Studies conducted by the National Institute of Health Sciences, announced the Surgeon General, had shown that NTA could combine with heavy metals and cause birth defects in rats. No more NTA. The industry should announce a "voluntary" agreement to stop using NTA at a press conference next morning. Into this confusion stepped the Senate committee on commerce, which issued a report *Advice to Consumers on Laundry Detergents*. The motto appearing at the beginning of this chapter is taken from it, and the report should be closely studied by diplomats, politicians, bureaucrats and all others in need to perfect the art of giving minimum information with a maximum of words. It is available for only 10 cents from the US Government Printing Office, Washington, DC 20402. For a mere dime one can buy no less than twenty-eight footnotes (for example, footnote 28 says "see footnote 6," and footnote 6 tells you to contact your state agency for water pollution) as well as a long appendix of addresses of water quality administrators in 50 states. Also included is the text, which contains such advice as that products which appear to reduce the flame retardant qualities "should not be used on flame-retardant fabrics unless the washing instructions with the garment say that they will not affect the finish." Housewives also receive the advice to try out for themselves just how much detergent is needed to get a clean wash.

When the dust had settled after all this commotion, it emerged very clearly that switching from phosphates to other substitutes was jumping from the frying pan into the fire. The streamers saying "Let's Be Eco-Logical" disappeared from the supermarkets, as did, for the most part, washing soda detergents from their shelves. The debates where one side would hurl "Eutrophication!" at the other, and the other would hurl back "Birth defects!" are forgotten. Government agencies which first pushed for NTA and then pulled in all directions are now competing in zeal to condemn non-phosphate substitutes. In May 1972, the National Institute of Environmental Health Sciences announced the results of a study of soap and non-phosphate detergents as eye irritants and found that some detergents using non-phosphates caused partial or total destruction of the cornea in New Zealand rabbits, and concluded that some of these detergents can cause irreversible blindness if rubbed into the eye. The Food and Drug Administration, however, has its own department to condemn the use of harmful ingredients in detergents, and such competition was not to be taken lightly. "They are treading outside the realm in which they should be operating," fumed an official of the FDA's Bureau of Product Safety, and he beat himself in the chest, "We have the charter, we have the mandate." He also asked the press not to be named, as it would violate protocol to criticize a sister agency (Associated Press, May 7, 1972).

And so the country is back to phosphates again to much the same extent as when the hullabaloo first started. Perhaps the only souvenir is the warning that must now be imprinted on detergent boxes cautioning against the health hazards of detergents when swallowed. The idea of warning pople old enough to read against eating detergents is, I suppose, another sign of the times. Not only does the world owe us a living, but it should also protect us poor idiots from the hazards we face as we stagger through life in a moronic stupor.

The inscription on detergent boxes is, of course, intended to protect children; but the philosophy behind it is not. It protects us poor idiots from thinking; we do not need brains when we have guidelines from those who know what is good for us. Do not the parents of a child have a responsibility to keep dangerous stuff out of its reach without being instructed by labels, warnings, laws, prohibitions, guidelines and directions? The auto safety fanatics say "If you send a tea cup through the mails, you pad and pack it well so it will not be damaged." Is a human driver a tea cup? Would it not be better to get the drunkards off the roads than to pad the railings in case they drive into them as they suckle the booze bottle?

Flammable Fabrics

Third Annual Report by U.S. Department of Health, Education, and Welfare

"Burn injuries constitute an extremely serious health problem in the United States. Such injuries associated with the ignition of clothing and other fabrics are, in most cases, more severe, more costly, and more often fatal than those not involving fabric ignition." This publication presents the third annual report to the President and Congress on the studies of death, injuries and economic losses resulting from accidental burning of products, fabrics, or related materials. 1972. 150 p. il. HE 20.4020:971 S/N 1712–0139 **$1.75**

What hysteria can do about algae. Most phosphate substitutes in detergents inactivated the flame-proof layer on inflammable fabrics. They also had many other adverse side effects more dangerous than algae.

What science can do about algae. Apart from filtering phosphates from sewage in water treatment plants, algae can also be destroyed by algicides, which in the hands of experts are both safe and effective. See *Algae in Water Supplies*, US Public Health Service, Division of Water Supply and Pollution Control (Public Health Service Publication no. 657, 1962), from which the two photos are taken. They show application of an algicide to a blanket of algae, and its subsequent disappearance after the test.

But back to phosphates. Was all this hullabaloo and confusion necessary? Of course not. A little research and rational analysis could have avoided what was due to yielding to the instant ecologists' half of the story. Algae in water supplies are a well researched subject, and a little listening to the experts and prudent decision making would soon have revealed the other half of the story of eutrophication.

And the other half of the story is that eutrophication is not caused by phosphates alone, nor can it arise under all conditions. Algae do not, for example, form in running waters. For many communities in the mountain states, the whole thing was a non-problem to begin with, yet they were stricken with the phosphate craze no less than the lakeside communities. For vast numbers of rural homes with septic tanks, phosphates only provided additional fertilization to the surrounding land with the outflow into the leech field; the guilt complex with which rural housewives were saddled was a hoax. Nor do algae live by phosphates alone. They live on a number of nutrients, of which phosphates come only in third place after nitrogen and carbon. If the water which supports them does not have enough of the other nutrients they need, they will die out no matter how much phosphor is present, just as a man will die of thirst without water, no matter how much food he has to save him from starvation. A little chemical analysis would have done more than rash action to appease the environmental shouters. Algae can be destroyed by safe and effective algicides, which have been known for many years (see p. 189). But most important of all, phosphates can be removed from the sewage in water treatment plants. The additional equipment for existing plants is technically feasible, though it is not cheap, as is so often the case with environmental problems. As in other cases, people will decide whether the benefits are worth the costs, and the minority will have to put up with the wishes of the majority, which is a decision making process that nobody has yet beaten — provided only that people are given all the facts enabling them to weigh their options.

This is the situation now. The situation tomorrow, in all reasonable expectation, is that phosphates will not keep their record of all-round favorable properties forever, and that the search for substitutes will eventually result in an effective cleaning material that neither causes eutrophication, nor threatens the health of its users, nor necessitates expensive additions to sewage treatment plants. But even now, the choice is not as narrow as either eutrophication or burning people alive. Once again, better technology, and not the lack of it, can provide the answers. The reversionists who want less technology and advocate a return to soap forget that it was detergents that solved the problem of high biological oxygen demand in the rivers and lakes into which too much starch and soap was discharged, for example, by the textile industry. The road back leads only to more filth and pollution. There was no lack of filth even before there was any textile industry, when people spun their own wool and wove their own fabrics; they were infested by lice and surrounded by rats.

But the phosphate flop has already done its damage. The housewife was first given a guilt complex for using phosphate detergents to get her laundry clean, not only by the cries of the environmental fanatics, but by official government agencies who gave in to their cries. Then, in September 1971, high government officials, including the Surgeon General and the head of the Food and Drug Administration, gave a press conference, in which they pointed to the health hazards of substitutes for phosphates. The Surgeon General suggested that for the time being housewives should use phosphate detergents, because they are safe for human health. Housewives felt, not surprisingly, that they had been made fools of. Can they be blamed if they regard some exotic Japanese diseases as just another hoax?

DDT

The controversy over DDT is not over, and the situation here is more complicated than in the case of phosphates. The debate is still raging, and the advocates of the continued, but reasonable use of DDT include such formidable figures as Nobel Prize winner Norman Borlaug and the World Health Organization, whilst the opponents of DDT are not helped by such freinds as Ehrlich or the Environmental Defense Fund, who have longe since lost their credibility by their unsubstantiated horror predictions. Nor has the recent ban of DDT by the Environmental Protection Agency in the United States done much to clarify the issue, for it was proclaimed shortly after other federal officials had given DDT a clean bill of health, and the decision to ban it was kept secret for some time, so that the US delegation at the environmental conference in Stockholm in June 1972 would have a rabbit to pull out of its hat when it was besieged on all sides on such issues as defoliation and "ecocide" in Viet Nam. Such a procedure cannot help raising the suspicion that the DDT issue was used as a political football.

However, questions of renown and reputation are not to the point. The opinions of a Nobel Prize winner and the recommendations of the World Health Organization are, in themselves, no proof. Experts have been wrong before, and laymen have been right before. In the last resort, the only reliable guide are the facts, and if these were less confusing, renowned scientists would not be at daggers over the issue.

The problem gained wide recognition through the publication of the late Rachel Carson's book *Silent Spring*. This book is often quoted as the beginning of the present ecocult. However, I find it hard to link its author with the present team of environmental fanatics. It is true that her book, too, starts with the gloomy prospect of American rural communities without birds, but that is a far cry from the fables by Dr. Ehrlich, whose visions litter America with corpses by the million. It is also true that many of her conclusions have been disputed, and some of them have been shown wrong. But unlike the later environmental literature, which advocates forced sterilization, triage, de-development and a stop to science and technology, Rachel Carson made a reasonable proposal for an alternative: biological control. It is not necessary, she argued, to use ever more toxic pesticides whose effectiveness is ever decreasing; if pests are a problem, control them by other species that are their natural enemies.

This appears a very reasonable argument, but there is, nevertheless, an inconsistency hidden in it, and on that inconsistency *Silent Spring* is silent. The problem of controlling the controllers is a very general one, and it appears in biological control just as it appears in chemical control; it even appears in politics and law enforcement. Rachel Carson, let alone her followers, did not consider the difference between reasonable chemical control and reasonable biological control on one hand, and chemical or biological overkill on the other. To her, and much more so to her followers, all chemical control is bad, and all biological control is good. They overlook that both types of control amount to man-sponsored interference with the environment; why should one type be always better than the other? The idea that reasonable chemical control need be no worse than reasonable biological control does not appear in *Silent Spring*, and it has never crossed the minds of the enemies of DDT.

The facts are, however, that biological control can get out of control more easily than chemical control. This is evident from the fact that the amounts of chemicals can be easily regulated, whereas a biological process, once started, can end in a vicious circle. Rachel Carson did not discover this method (nor did she make such a claim); it has been known for a long time, because it was the only known method of pest control before effective chemicals were discovered. And the experience with them is the same as with any other form of control: If the controller gets out of control, you merely have a new problem on your hands.

In the last century, there was an abundance of poisonous snakes in Jamaica. To control this pest, a natural enemy of snakes was imported: the secretary bird of Africa, a member of the falcon family. The snakes were indeed brought under control, but what got out of control were the field rats, which had hitherto been eaten by the snakes. The damage to the sugar plantations was such that the British had to look round for a new natural enemy, and they found one in the Indian mongoose. They brought no more than four pairs of mongooses from India, and the mongooses rapidly multiplied on the diet of rats, almost totally exterminating them. But in ten years' time, Jamaica had a new pest on its hands — the Indian mongoose. When they ran out of rats, they ate up every other small animal they could find — including puppies, goat kids, piglets, and poultry and its eggs. And all this resulted only from four pairs of mongooses! The British, as the Czech saying goes, had used Satan to drive out Lucipher. Perhaps due to the Jamaican experience, it is now illegal to import the mongoose into the United States. Wyoming is probably better off with its rattlesnakes than with another pest that might control them.

Many other such cases are known. The rabbit is not native to Australia, but was brought there from Europe at the end of the 18th century. Australian farmers paid a bounty on every tail of a killed rabbit, and when that proved insufficient, they artificially propagated an epidemic of a disease that broke out among some rabbits, and diseased bodies were later brought to other countries in an effort to infect rabbits. The sparrow is another example of how quickly a species can multiply. It was absent from the New World until it was brought over from Europe. In Hawaii, it has displaced many or most of the smaller birds.

These are not horror stories of the future, but experiences from the past. They are mentioned here, not in an attempt to discredit biological control of any kind, but to point out that biological control suffers from the same problem of controlling the controller as does chemical control; in fact, if four pairs of mongooses can result in what happened in Jamaica, it seems very plausible that the nozzle of the jet spraying pesticides from an aircraft is not at all a bad way to control the controller. The question seems to be not whether chemical pesticides should be used at all, but whether they need to be thrown around by the ton from squadrons of aircraft.

Like everything else, DDT has advantages and disadvantages, and these must rationally be weighed in a given set of conditions; extremism usually entails disadvantages under all conditions. There is some dispute as to the dangers of DDT, even if used recklessly; but there is no dispute at all as to the calamities that have followed when its use was recklessly discontinued.

Once in a long while, men discover how to synthesize chemical compounds that alleviate or eliminate human suffering on a truly historic scale. The discovery of anaesthetics in the last century was such a discovery. The discovery of DDT during World War II was another. Its benefits are too well known to be repeated here; suffice it to say that the number of malaria cases in Ceylon dropped from 2.8 million in 1946 to 110 in 1961 after countrywide spraying with DDT, and the number of deaths was reduced from 12,587 to none at all.

The opponents of DDT point, above all, to its persistency. That claim is not altogether true, since it has been shown that DDT is decomposed by sea water; but even so, persistency is not, in itself, a danger unless the persistent material is harmful as well. And here the arguments begin to get onto very shaky ground. Most of the "what if" theories and fantasies have been refuted. In spite of intensive research by many scientific institutions, including the US Public Health Service, not the slightest evidence has been found that DDT causes cancer, as feared by Rachel Carson, and asserted by her followers. In fact, DDT has never been shown harmful to people at all, although the point has been carefully investigated. A California couple were reported (*Time*, August 1971) to start breakfast with a 10 mg capsule of DDT every morning, and after 93 days they had ingested as much as persons consuming food dusted with the pesticide would get in 83 years, but the couple noted no ill effects; this is given here as an illustration, not as a scientific proof.

The fact that DDT moves up the food chains and can now be found in exceedingly minute quantities in human fat is no argument against DDT, for not only do tests show these amounts harmless, but there is some evidence that it gets into the bloodstream and is eventually discharged from the body.

There is, however, some evidence that DDT is harmful to a few forms of wildlife, in particular, some species of marine life and fish-eating birds. What has been established, for example, is that the eggshells of some pelicans are too weak to be hatched, and though this evidence has been disputed by some who claim that the cause is not necessarily DDT, it seems that the opponents of DDT now have the better of the argument. However, the environmentalists overlook two points even if it is granted that the charge is correct. First, they have not weighed the pros and cons when they clamor for prohibition of DDT on such grounds alone. Not all people are satisfied that the life of a pelican has the same value as that of a human being, which might be saved from an insect-carried disease. In any case, we have met such theoretical dilemmas before, and it always turned out that the dilemma had more than two horns. This is the case here, too, for the second point is that such evidence has been produced only in North America, showing that the phenomenon is a local one. Only in North America (and perhaps Sweden) has DDT been used recklessly by the ton without heed what will happen to the DDT that falls where it is not needed.

But whilst the arguments against DDT, and even against its reckless use, are hotly contested, there can be no doubt about what happens if it is recklessly withdrawn. In the United States, where malaria is not a significant problem, the reckless withdrawal of all pesticides has had other effects whenever it occurred. Brainwashed by the clamor of the environmentalists, residents of many areas from Maine to New Jersey voted to ban all pesticides, including DDT, which had been used to spray the forests. It harmed beneficial insects and some birds, the environmentalists claimed, and even though the population of the gypsy moth had been known to rise during 1970, the environmentalists had their way in many areas. Their hopes of avoiding a Silent Spring were not disappointed. The spring of 1971 was not silent. The noise of millions of gypsy moth larvae chewing up the woodlands, together with the noise of falling leaves and the drizzle of the moths' excrement was, according to the chief of Massachusetts' bureau of insect control, awe-inspiring. Almost 1,000,000 acres of forests were denuded and it remains to be seen how many trees did not keep their strength to survive such an attack. The possible consequences of using too much DDT are still being hotly contested, but there is nothing to be debated in what happened in New England in 1971. The photographs of defoliated woods from Maine to New Jersey make a fool out of anybody who would dispute the effect.

There is a number of lessons in the not-so-silent spring of 1971. The environmental fanatics tried to save a few birds on the grounds of contested theories; they ended up destroying these birds' habitat. Try as they may, the environmental fanatics can never crawl out of their self-defeating circles, whether the circle involves the gypsy moth or nuclear power stations.

Second, the gypsy moth is another example of the dangers of biological control, especially if it is regarded as a panacea under all conditions and as a universal substitute for chemical pesticides. The gypsy moth is not native to North America, but was imported to Massachusetts in 1869 from Europe by Leopold Trouvelot, a naturalist who hoped to crossbreed the moths with silkworms. The millions or billions of larvae that chewed up the New England forests in 1971 were all descendants of the handful of gypsy moths that Trouvelot brought over. How does one control such an outburst once it is started? On this type of population explosion, the pundits of the ecocult write no books called *The Population Explosion*. The gypsy moth has no effective natural enemies known to man; but presumably they are known to nature, and an outburst of one species usually attracts and feeds the species of its enemy. As we have seen before, the checks and balances of nature are not at all delicate; in this case, it is to be hoped that they are quick.

The third point is that "ecological backlash" did not fail to appear; no sane person will vote a second time for a man subscribing to cute theories which result in a million acres of defoliated woodlands. In the fall of 1971, all candidates for political office in Bristol, Connecticut, for example, were campaigning under the same slogan: Spray pesticides! They did not, of course, campaign to spray them reasonably and with moderation.

The ban on DDT in the United States which took effect in 1972 is not as reckless as the bans that led to the woods of the North East being denuded, because it permits certain non-persistent pesticides as substitutes. But already the environmental fanatics have filed suits against the ban on the grounds that it is not strict enough. The result of this situation cannot be long in coming. Farmers and landowners will no longer throw pesticides around by the ton. They will throw them around by the hundreds of tons while the going is good.

Defoliated woods on Cape Cod, part of almost one million acres of woodland that were defoliated in New England in the spring of 1971 by gypsy moth larvae after many communities had banned DDT and other chemical pesticides.

Farmers and landowners are not sadists who would use more pesticides than necessary just for the joy of damaging the environment, and they are not likely to waste money on extra tons of chemical pesticides. But what will make them so sure that the money is wasted? Not the environmentalists who raved against pesticides until almost a million acres of woodlands were denuded in New England. If the farmers and landowners have any doubts whether to use more or less than last time, they will be quickly scared into using more by the unthinking propaganda of the Friends of the Earth and the Environmental Defense Fund.

The debate on DDT continues. The World Health Organization is following the point closely and issues occasional reports on the question of DDT. The last report of which I know (October 1971) states that sudden and wholesale withdrawal of DDT as an insecticide would be a major disaster. It also points to some dangers of its abuse and does not recommend its use to be continued indefinitely; it recommends a search for substitutes. In malaria control, for example, the two substitutes that are close to the effectiveness of DDT without being persistent have other drawbacks: Both are less safe to handle, and one (malathion) would treble the cost of malaria spraying programs, whilst the other (propoxur) would increase the cost by a factor of almost nine.

Dr. Norman E. Borlaug, the father of the "Green Revolution," points out that this revolution could not have taken place without DDT and even now there is nothing realistic in sight to take the place of DDT in breaking the vicious circles of poverty and disease to arrive at a healthier crop tended by a healthier force of workers. "The scare tactics used by the Environmental Defense Fund," says Dr. Borlaug in a debate printed in the daily press (December 1971), "based on unsubstantiated scientific data, questionable ethics, emotion and oratory, have been used very effectively for raising funds and gaining support for their battle against DDT . . . One of their advertisements in the New York Times headlined 'Is Mother's Milk Fit for Human Consumption?' was especially effective. It stated that DDT had been found in mother's milk. No mention was made of the fact it was present at very low levels. Of course no mention was made of the fact that caffein, nicotine or alcohol in small quantities might also be present in mother's milk when she drinks coffee, smokes cigarettes or drinks cocktails. Nevertheless, the report of detection of DDT in mother's milk provoked indignation and brought in much financial support."

Such demagogical halftruth advertisements do little to clarify the case against DDT for persons who wish to examine the evidence rather than the state of mind of the accuser. Since most opponents of DDT come from the ranks of the ecohysterical organizations, it is quite difficult to weed out the serious objections among the stacks of cancer scares and holocausts by DDT pollution. Nevertheless, the reader willing to go through pages of emotional drivel will find such arguments. Malaria in the underdeveloped countries is one thing, and thin-shelled eggs of pelicans in California is another, say some, and here they do have a point; the case for differentiated decisions is no doubt reasonable and deserves consideration. Another reasonable proposal is to use alternative methods of pest control, but these proposals are rarely implemented by realistic suggestions what exactly these alternatives should be. The Environmental Defense Fund, for example, advocates substitutes that are not "a human health hazard," and in flat contradiction to the US Public Health Service states that DDT is a human health hazard. Once more, a reasonable idea becomes unreasonable as it goes off on a tangent to fight a nonexistent threat. Moreover, the opponents of DDT are almost invariably opposed to *all* chemical pesticides, which makes the search for a realistic substitute for insect control even harder. "Some day it may be possible to use alternate non-chemical methods to control many of the insects responsible for the most severe crop and animal losses," says Dr. Borlaug, "but that day, if ever attainable, lies far in the future. Today, however, conventional insecticides are needed to control 80 to 90% of the insect problems affecting agricultural and public health."

I cannot, of course, take a stand on an issue over which the qualified experts are still strongly divided. Nor is this a book of recipes and verdicts. The example of DDT was given here not to prove that DDT is harmless, but to show how self-defeating environmental hysterics are in this case as in the others. Whatever arguments there are against DDT (and there may be many) have been reduced to invisibility by the mountains of garbage that the environmental fanatics have piled over them; they have given the qualified allies of their cause a kiss of death.

But the reputation of the environmental fanatics leaves me very cold. The point of interest here is that their shaky theories are theories, and the defoliation of New England forests in 1971 is a fact. Their shaky theories have also resulted in another fact: The almost total ban on DDT by the Environmental Protection Agency, in contradiction to the clean bill of health, including that of wildlife, given to DDT by other federal officials. It is too early to observe the results of that ban; but it is a ban that risks replacement of tons of DDT by hundreds of tons of other chemicals. It seems likely that one extreme has been replaced by another and that moderation and reasonable weighing of the options under different circumstances have lost out to the clamor of the faddists. A victory has been won for the louse.

GENETIC ENGINEERING

The fears and fantasies of those who usually know no more than the two words *genetic engineering* are so absurd and ludicrous that at first I was at a loss whether to discredit this book by even mentioning the insane science fiction that has been served to an unsuspecting public as the reality of tomorrow, but a recent issue of the *Saturday Review* changed my mind. Whilst the sick fantasies bloom with acrobatic diversity, they all lead to the same conclusion: Scientists are aspiring to Godhood, and they must be stopped before it is too late.

The facts, which are ignored in these fantasies with boring monotony, are very sobering. One is that genetic engineering, in the sense of people taking action to ensure the best possible qualities in their offspring, is almost as old as mankind. Another is that "cloning," or the sexless reproduction of a living organism with all its genetic properties, has been performed in the case of carrots and some other plants. The greatest success thus far achieved with animals is one where the unfertilized eggs of a frog were implanted with a cell taken from the intestines of the same animal. The tadpoles and frogs which developed from the egg thus stimulated were reproduced without the benefit of the other sex, so that they had the genetic characteristics of only one parent. That does not make it a Xerox machine. To do the same kind of thing with mammals, let alone human beings, is as far removed from frogs' eggs as the computer is from the wheel, and even then the process and its results bear no resemblance to the science fiction passed off as facts.

Aldous Huxley was an able scientist (his brother Julian was a great biologist), and when he wrote *Brave New World*, he had a point to make, but he made no attempt to claim that his book was anything but a novel. A recent article in the *Saturday Review* had no such compunctions.* The cover of the issue shows a baby in a flask labeled ENGINEER MALE/I.Q. 160-#79314B, and an inside page is covered with an endless pattern of such flasks; a further page shows the same flask and label, but the engineer in its liquid is now grown up, complete with wristwatch and slide-rule. Science Fiction? A satire? Not at all. The authors are deadly serious. "The technology

---

* J.V. Tunney and M.E. Levine, *Genetic Engineering*, Saturday Review, August 5, 1972, pp. 23-28.

for the cloning of human beings might be available within anything from ten to twenty-five years." Period. "The technology for *in vitro* fertilization and for reimplantation in human beings should be available within five to ten years, or perhaps even earlier." Period. The authors give no indication in how many years we may expect the Invisible Man or Superman's X-ray vision.

Judging from these and other hair-raising predictions (freely mixed with true items, such as "test-tube babies"), it seems highly improbable that the authors have seen a biology book even as it may have fallen past their window. More likely, they have been duped into panic on reading a cover story in *Time*, envisaging mathematics departments of Albert Einsteins and entire police forces of Edgar J. Hoovers. One might perhaps continue *Time*'s fantasies: These Edgar J. Hoovers could be crossed with wolves so that they could howl and imploit the metal otherwise needed for police whistles, and perhaps a chromosome or two of a housefly might be added to the genetic soup, so that these Edgar J. Hoovers could see in all directions and spot the Joseph V. Stalins hiding under the table, or maybe even under the carpet if they have been engineered with the genes of flatworms.

But the abyss between the unfertilized eggs of an amphibian and those of higher mammals does not disturb the ignorant pompousness of such unintended comedy; it can be bridged easily enough with printing ink. Whilst scientists are still trying to understand sexless reproduction in carrots and frogs, the authors of the article in the *Saturday Review* rush in with such questions as these: Do genes have civil rights? Does genetic engineering presume a concept of "optimum" man? Will the quest for improvement make all children "superior" to their parents? Should research be pursued that will give scientists the genetic capability to engineer human beings?

And the inevitable conclusion: "The issues raised by the biomedical scientists must be debated, and the debate must begin now. If we postpone the debate in this area, we might face irreversible trends not only in genetics but also in political freedoms... The issues raised require interdisciplinary attention. We cannot begin too soon to debate them." [Oh no?]

The authors' frantic waving of the Bill of Rights and the US Constitution is not only absurdly premature, it is also quixotic. Liberty and the pursuit of happiness surely also means the right of parents to ensure the best possible qualities in their offspring. Genetic engineering in that sense (and there is no other sense, except abuse, which is not peculiar to genetic engineering) is older than civilization. Most cultures, no matter how primitive, forbid incest. Is that not genetic engineering? When a pregnant mother foregoes smoking and alcohol for the sake of her baby, is that not genetic engineering? When state laws require blood tests before a marriage license is granted, is that not genetic engineering? When couples decide not to beget any children because blood tests show that they have incompatible rhesus factors, is that not genetic engineering?

There is, nevertheless, one interesting aspect in all this hullabaloo about genetic engineering, which is used as one more bugaboo against "too much science," and which is water onto the mill of the technophobes and science baiters. The population controllers who would sterilize people against their will and forbid diabetics to have children, the triage proponents who would starve whole nations to death, the environmental fanatics who cause pollution and human suffering by their sabotage of needed power stations, the econuts who want to protect the environment from flood control, the eco-freaks to whom amoebae are more important than human beings, the whole benighted crowd of them raise their finger to heaven and unite in one heart-rending cry: "Morality!"

AND MORE FOOLISHNESS

This book cannot go on forever, which is what it would have to do if it were to examine every paper tiger produced by the technophobes and environmental fanatics who confront us with a new paper tiger long before their last one is exposed as another hoax. Shifting the burden of proof of their idiotic "what if" theories to the rest of the world is, in fact, the tactic which keeps the ecocult going. In choosing among these paper tigers I have not chosen the ones that are most easily defeated, but the ones that seem to have had the greatest effect in fanning the hysteria. Hard as it may be to believe, there are more radical advocates of population control and de-development than Dr. Ehrlich, and strange as it may seem, there are more ludicrous computer programs than the ones used in the Club of Rome's doomsday machine. But it is hoped that the more effective examples of paper tigers discussed in the preceding chapters have made the point, and that I will not be expected to take on the impossible task of dealing with every fantastic theory published in the literature of technophobia, ecohysteria and apocalypse.

Among the less boring of such fantasies is the claim that supersonic transport planes could lead to a state where living creatures would have to go underground or be blinded. What is remarkable about this cataclysmic chain leading via supersonic transport planes and disintegration of the ozon layer to ultraviolet radiation blinding everything but moles is that it was made, not in the comic books, which nowadays are also highly conscious of the environment, but by a scientist, and that it was used as one of the arguments in the emotional debate that resulted in shooting down the SST. This ingenious theory of the mole effect was de-molished in Stockholm in July 1971 by a conference of scientists devoted to man's impact on the climate, and the details can be found in any college library.

Babies should be washed only with soap and water, for if that was good enough for their great-grandmothers, it must be good enough for them. A fiendish thing like hexachlorophene is dangerous, for its name is reminiscent of chemistry, and it is too long, anyway. Disinfectants are not ecological. "I told you so!" triumphed Mrs. Econut when the FDA found hexachlorophene to cause brain damage in some laboratory animals. The meaning, if any, of effects on lower mammals when subjected to mammoth overdoses of certain chemicals is a point under lively discussion, but the FDA apparently left no doubt in its public warning to 600,000 doctors, hospitals, nurses and health institutions that the use of hexachlorophene for washing and bathing babies should immediately be discontinued. This was announced on December 6, 1971; six weeks later, a nationwide survey began to collect data on the skin infection outbreaks reported by the nurseries of hospitals all over the country. A meeting of the representatives of the FDA, the Environmental Protection Agency, the National Center for Disease Control and the American Academy of Pediatrics was called. Hospitals had misunderstood the government warning, an FDA spokesman explained lamely. The ban applied only to babies' bodies, not to the hexachlorophene used by doctors and nurses for scrubbing their hands before they handle them. Not everybody found such logic consistent, but it is really quite simple: It is only a matter of interpreting correctly what exactly it means when mice and guinea pigs go gaga.

It has become common to lay the blame for all such mishaps at the door of the FDA, but this is not fair, since the FDA is bound by law to prohibit any food additives that have been shown to cause cancer in humans and animals. This was the reason why cyclamates were banned in 1970, although the evidence in that case was extremely flimsy, and the head of the FDA was very reluctant at the congressional hearings on cyclamates to give a clear-cut answer whether or not such a connection had been established. To be on the safe side, these artificial sweeteners were banned anyway, and for a time "contains no cyclamates" became the advertising cry of many food products, including some that had no reason to use artificial sweeteners in the first place. But the irony of it was (and is) that the additives used long before the FDA came into being are not subject to any such tests. One of such additives is sacharine, the older type of sweetener, and there is no firm evidence that sacharine and other "old" additives are less dangerous than the newer additives that are now banned. There are no FDA tests comparing sacharine and cyclamates; the law does not require sacharine to be tested.

Sacharine is, in fact, one of the fields that have not yet been grazed by the econuts, though it should prove no less fertile for their run-away imaginations than the fields they have so far entered. It has, for example, never been conclusively disproved that sacharine may lead to St. Vitus dance in baboons; equally sinister are the possibilities that it might cause haemorrhoids in sea horses. And these are only the beginning of the wild cause-effect chains leading to doom, because the sea horses fed on sacharine will ultimately make the galaxies fly apart. As a matter of fact, the galaxies are flying apart already, and one shudders to think of the chain reaction that will start when one day an econut should look into a book on astronomy.

7

The Real Dangers

The age of innocent faith in science and technology may be over.
Barry Commoner, *Science and Survival* (1966).

We learned the meaning of scientific double-talk. We learned that when the scientists said "We have no evidence that DDT is harmful to humans" they meant that the study was still in progress and we were the experimental animals.
Garrett De Bell, *Environmental Handbook*, (1970).

The scope of the preceding chapters was essentially limited to rebuttals of the arguments of the ecocult; in particular, the discussion attempted to show that what is needed to ensure a clean environment is more technology, not less.

But rebuttals of the one-sided arguments of the ecocult tend to become one-sided themselves unless the problem is considered in its entirety. Such a general analysis would go far beyond the scope of this book, whose main purpose is to demonstrate the absurdity of the ecocult's recipes. Nevertheless, it should not be concluded that the wider societal problems do not exist merely because they have not been discussed here. In particular, the attention focused on technology should not be interpreted as a philosophy that technology is an almighty and omnipotent God able to cure all ills of society. Such one-sided thinking, or thoughtlessness, would be all too reminiscent of the simplistic prejudices of the ecocult.

Superior technology is certainly a necessary condition for a healthy society, but it is just as certainly not sufficient by itself. Not only can technology by itself not cure such ills as crime, drug addiction or bureaucratic thoughtlessness, but it cannot even, by itself, cure such ills as pollution. With the possible exception of replacing the present automobile by a vehicle of *equal performance*, technology stands ready to eliminate pollution; but it can do very little about the problem of who is going to pay the bill. That problem will eventually be decided by the democratic process, which will require people to weigh costs against benefits, and this, in turn, will require them to know the facts and available options. The thing that is needed least in such decisions is emotional oratory.

I do not intend to abandon the limited scope of this book in this concluding consideration. Nor do I propose to replace mindless pessimism by mindless optimism. I merely wish to point out some dangers which in my opinion (and it is only an opinion) are inherent in the present evolution of the ecocult.

Many scientists believe that there are no such dangers. They point to the fact that the environmentalists have done a good job in drawing public attention to problems whose solution has long been overdue — a point that I will readily concede — and that the extremist aspects of the ecocult will be cured by a few blackouts of the coming energy shortage. They recommend reading Dr. Ehrlich's books in the spirit in which one reads Art Buchwald's delightful column, and they dismiss the Club of Rome's computer program as GIGO (garbage in, garbage out).

If I shared their optimism, this book would not have been written. It is my opinion (not necessarily a fact) that there are three dangers which the ecocult may involve: more pollution of the environment, a significant weakening of national security, and the subversion of science.

THE idea of protecting and preserving man's environment is one with which no sane man can quarrel. There can be little doubt that the early environmentalists did a good thing in focusing public attention to the evils of pollution and mindless destruction of the environment.

Is this still what motivates the ecological and environmental organizations? History is full of movements, large and small, significant and petty, which started with a great idea only to degenerate into something very different when the movement became dominated by the True Believers. Christian brotherly love became the rationale for the torture chambers of the Inquisition. Liberty, equality, fraternity were the words shouted around the guillotine as the French Revolution devoured its own children in a grim reign of terror. Karl Marx's theory of how to rid the proletarian of his chains became the official philosophy of the most powerful repressive empire known to history. The crusaders against alcohol found an improbable ally in their efforts to prolong prohibition: the bootlegger. The crusader against pornography is an unwitting ally of the pornographer, who profits from the desire for the forbidden, and the crusader himself ends up in the committee gaping at all the dirty pictures.

The ecocult shows all the signs of a degenerating movement which started with good intentions. The original idea of clean air, clean water, conservation of nature and improved quality of life still figures in the ecocult's literature, just as human rights still figure in the Soviet constitution; but this idea has been heavily overshadowed by the principle of technophobia and stopping scientific advance under penalty of doomsday. The blind opposition to nuclear power stations, to hydroelectric plants, and the many other cures of easing the blood pressure by beheading the patient bear this out every time there is a choice between technological advance or stunting the growth of technology.

What, for example, have the environmental organizations done since the *Torrey Canyon* ran aground off the coast of Cornwall in 1967 and spilled 117,000 tons of crude oil? Nothing except disseminate horror stories of how the Cornish coast would never be the same again and marine life would be gone for decades (it was back to normal within 6 months, and only an expert ornithologist can now find traces of the disaster). Did they lift a finger toward the research on detergents, fire bombs and chalk dust to sink and absorb oil spills? Did they call for the agreements that have since been hammered out in international maritime organizations to prevent such spills? Did they call for research on better sources of energy than fuels? No, that is not their business; their business is technophobia: They are waiting for the day when one of the supertankers will break in two so that they can shout "We told you so!" They want no oil and no supertankers at all.

Other movements have failed because they considered the means more important than the end. The environmental fanatics have so hypnotized themselves into technophobia that they have forgotten the end altogether.

The looming energy crisis, which in one form or another can hardly be averted now, is a crisis which is not due to a lack of energy, but to a lack of facilities to harness the energy resources which are available. That access has to a large extent been blocked by the environmental fanatics. By the time this book is published, the Alaska pipeline could already have been supplying 2 bbl. of oil a day, or about one eighth of the total US oil consumption. It will be built with environmental safeguards bordering on the absurd, but whenever the last of the environmentalists' obstructions is finally overcome, it will take three more years to build it. Thousands and thousands of megawatts of electric power produced without an ounce of pollution by nuclear and hydroelectric plants would be available now if the construction of power plants had not been sabotaged by the environmental organizations' legalistic guerilla tactics; the examples of these non-polluting power stations show perhaps better than anything else that the environmental organizations are not in the business of preventing pollution, but in the business of blind opposition to all technology.

Will the energy crisis make people call for more power as fast as it can be generated, even if the quickest way is fossil-burning plants that pollute? Will it persuade them that "technology got us into this mess"? Will it make them settle for a smaller energy consumption? I am not as well versed in predictions as the gurus of the ecocult, and I have no answer to such questions. Much of the enormous waste of power in the United States will doubtlessly provide a shock absorber. But the most likely road in a crisis is the easiest road. When a kilowatt-hour of electric power costs 80 cents and a gallon of gas costs a dollar, there will be "enough" for everybody. This is, in effect, what the de-developers recommend. If so, the hardest hit will be the poor; but then, environmentalism and compassion with the poor have been on a collision course for some time.

The other immediate and easy way is to import the energy, particularly gas and oil, from abroad. With large supplies of natural gas untapped in the United States, it is already being imported in liquid form from Algeria. With the Alaska pipe line tied up in unending litigation, the United States is now importing about one half of its oil needs. About one third of this comes from sources well within reach of Soviet claws, or with the Soviet grasp already accomplished. In June 1972, after the Iraqui government had seized the Western-owned Iraq Petroleum Company with strong Soviet encouragement and hints that the Soviets would buy the oil if the West did not continue to buy it, Radio Moscow made the following comment on American oil imports:

Up to a third of it will be carried from the Middle East to the United States — but the scale of the national liberation movement of the peoples of Asia and the Middle East is inflicting blows to the predatory plans of the American monopolists.

National liberation movement, in Brezhnevspeak, refers to the sheiks and dictators who rule the Arab world, whose population lives in abysmal poverty and ignorance.

But what about the other two thirds? They come from sources not yet within Soviet reach, mainly from South America. Here, the life lines of oil are protected by the supremacy of the US Navy on the seas — or are they? Since the Soviets lost out in Cuba due to insufficient sea power, they have been building their navy at a feverish pace unknown to naval history. They are building warships at three times the rate of the United States; they often retire them as obsolete in 10 years, whilst the average age of US ships (Sixth Fleet) is about 19 years; their guided missile cruisers are more modern and they already outnumber American cruisers; their submarines outnumber American submarines by more than 2 : 1. It is not likely that the Soviets will commit nuclear suicide; but how about the little encroachments here and the little aggressions there? Step by little step is what got the Soviets ahead along their road of conquest and enslavement. The alliance of environmental fanatics and blind pacifists is not only blocking the Alaska pipeline, it is also denying the US Navy the appropriations it is asking for; the horrors and hypocrisy of the Viet Nam war have led them, by a rare somersault of logic, to the conclusion that *all* things connected with defense and the military are bad.

Whilst this threat to security is probably the most dangerous aspect of the ecocult, there is also another aspect which, in my opinion, is a significant threat of a quite different type. It is the threat to subvert science from within.

A scientist is essentially a man searching for the truth. A man who has already found his version of the truth and is merely searching for one-sided evidence to prop it up is at best an ex-scientist. If he is doing this because he has tied himself up in his own little pet theory, he is no threat to science; this kind of thing happens all the time, and the scientist to whom this happens merely finds himself left in the ditch by the wayside.

Nor is the scientist who is in error in his search for truth a threat to science; on the contrary, the history of science is full of errors and their refutations. Scientists are not infallible, and the only scientist who has never been wrong is the one who has no publications. The truth, very often, is what remains when all errors have been demolished in clashes of opinion. Such errors, clashes and the emerging truth, far from being a threat to science, is what drives science forward.

The charges of scientists aspiring to Godhood and overstepping their bounds are not a threat to science, either. Science has always worked on the frontiers of knowledge, and stepping over this frontier is what science is about. Working with the unknown has always been considered as something sinister, especially by anti-intellectuals. They would not suspect a baker of putting poison in his bread, because they have a rough idea how bread is baked; but they suspect the biologist engaged in genetic engineering of doing something fiendish, because they have no idea what cloning really means. This type of attack from the outside has been with science from the beginning of its recorded history, and it is not likely to develop into a serious threat.

But none of these cases have the element that has been absent from science for a hundred years (for three hundred years in the exact sciences) and that has appeared with the ecocult: scientists who make their results conform to a common philosophy, shared by an interdisciplinary group. It is questionable whether the figure on p. 159 is a mere mistake by objective scientists in search of truth. It raises the suspicion that the people who used it were not looking for the truth, because they had already found it; they may have found these partial data convenient in their search for one-sided evidence to prop up such an alleged and preconceived truth. And it conforms not to one of the individual hobby horses that some scientists are riding all by themselves, but to a general doomsday philosophy which some ex-scientists have embraced. Manipulation or one-sided search for data to conform to a general philosophy is a disturbing phenomenon.

When Galileo Galilei threw the leaden and wooden balls from the leaning tower of Pisa to show that gravitational acceleration is independent of mass, one of the balls was an inch or so behind the other (evidently due to the imperfect simultaneity of dropping them or the imperfect equality in aerodynamic resistance). That inch was used by his opponents to reject the experiment. They were slaves to the philosophy of Aristotle, who taught that experimentation was unworthy of human intellect and that the speed of falling objects was proportional to their weight. Is this not reminiscent of holding on to the doomsday philosophy by using data as shown in the figures on pp. 159-161 or attacking the Green Revolution on the grounds that agricultural machinery and pesticides are costly?

When Darwin's teachings contradicted the literal interpretation of the Bible, some scientists abandoned their search for truth in favor of a search for one-sided evidence to disprove the theory of evolution. They became ex-scientists and slaves to a philosophy. Until the advent of the ecocult, they were also the last group of scientists to whom this happened. Neither the Nazis nor the Soviets, for example, succeeded to any significant degree in making scientists produce data conforming to their philosophies. Nazi textbooks on physics called Einstein a Jewish swindler, but they used his equations nevertheless. Zhdanov called cybernetics and quantum mechanics bourgeois pseudo-sciences, but he could get only a few philosophers to parrot him and he found no physicist to back him up. I am not, of course, comparing the ecocult to the Nazis or the Soviets; I am comparing scientists who are slaves to a philosophy. Their data are manipulated to produce doomsday; they are prophets of a faith, not investigators of a science.

Moreover, we are today witnessing calls to stop science from going too far not only from amateurs and anti-intellectuals, who have been singing this song for two and a half thousand years. Some scientists, or ex-scientists, who have become converts of the doomsday philosophy have now joined in this chorus, although there is not a single scientific discovery, from the wheel to atomic energy, that cannot be used for both good and bad purposes.

The fact that scientific data are being collected in order to conform to a general philosophy, and that they are sometimes collected by ex-scientists, are two of the differences between the ecocult and other fads like flying saucers (few of which have been sighted since ecology became the fashion). They are also, in my opinion, two danger signals. I am not irrevocably convinced that science must always win. The high level of science in the ancient world was swept away by the mysticism and dogmatism of the Middle Ages, and it took a millenium (in the exact sciences) to reach that level again. I am not suggesting that this will happen again, and I certainly do not want to counter the environmental paranoia by paranoia of another kind. I am merely suggesting that the survival of unbiased science is nowhere guaranteed.

Flying saucers or squaring the circle are harmless fads that enchant many people and do little damage to the others.

But the ecocult is not harmless. It has already led to more pollution by opposition to new and superior power plants; it has already led to a curtailment of scientific activity; it has already blocked access to resources and energy; it has already succeeded in making a perceptible section of the high school and college generation distrust science and scientists; it has already succeeded in moulding a widespread opinion that science and technology must be curbed; it has already succeeded in substantially decreasing the enrolment of young people in the study of physics and engineering.

We are therefore not concerned with an amusing obsession, with flying saucers, with California sinking into the sea overnight, or with this or that erroneous theory.

This time, science itself is under attack.

Index